Welcome to A Year with **Yours** 2015 – I can guarantee you are in for a treat! This fabulous book is packed full of features to keep you entertained and inspired throughout the year ahead.

We've got practical advice to help you stay healthy, seasonal gardening tips and horoscopes for the year ahead. There's plenty to read too, with childhood memories, evocative nostalgic photographs and exclusive short stories.

And, if you're looking for inspiration, we've got ideas for days out, seasonal craft projects and a new recipe to try every week of the year.

This book is created with the help of **Yours** readers – it's their stories that make it so special – so, sincere thanks to all who contributed, including those whose letters we didn't have room to publish.

Happy reading – and all the best for 2015

Sharon

Sharon Reid
Editor, **Yours** Magazine

Published by Pedigree in association with **Yours**
Pedigree Books Limited, Beech House, Walnut Gardens, Exeter, Devon EX4 4DH

Yours – the read of your life every fortnight! Look out for it in your local newsagent.
Yours, Bauer London Lifestyle, Media House, Peterborough Business Park, Peterborough PE2 6EA.
Tel: 01733 468000

Compiled and edited by Sharon Reid
Designed by David Reid
Sub-edited by Christine Curtis
Additional writing by Marion Clarke, Michelle Nightingale, Alex Frisby, Laura Bradder,
Lizzy Denning and Rebecca Speechley
Story illustrations by Kate Burgess

◆ All telephone numbers, website details and dates correct at time of going to press

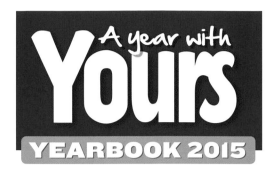

Name
Address
Postcode
Home phone
Mobile phone
Email

In case of emergency, contact

Name
Telephone

Useful contacts

Bank	
Building society	
Chemist/pharmacy	
Chiropodist	
Council	
Credit card emergency	
Dentist	
Doctor	
Electrician	
Garage	
Hairdresser	
Hospital	
Local police	
Milkman	
Optician	
Plumber	
Solicitor	
Taxi	
Vet	

Renewal reminders

	Renewal date	Policy number	Telephone
Car insurance			
Car tax			
MOT			
Home insurance			
TV licence			
Pet insurance			
Yours subscription			

THE YEAR AHEAD

Your top-to-toe guide to a healthy 2015

If good health is top of your New Year wish list then this guide is all you need to stay in great shape this year

Boost your brain power

If you'd like to keep your memory sharp and your brain healthy think about how you look after your heart. Scientists believe that your heart health and your brain health are closely linked, and that what's good for your heart is good for your brain too. Studies have found that you could reduce your risk of heart disease by 70 per cent and your changes of cognitive decline by 60 per cent by making these five lifestyle changes.

1 Follow a healthy diet

A diet packed full of fruit and vegetables, wholegrains, lean protein and essential fats and fewer portions of fatty, sugary foods could help to reduce your risk of dementia.

Studies have found that omega-3 fatty acids in oily fish and olive oil may help to prevent your brain from shrinking as you age.

And you could further reduce your risk by 21 per cent by upping your fruit and veg intake, according to another study.

2 Exercise your body

The current guidelines suggest that we should all be doing 30 minutes of exercise five times a week. Find something you really enjoy to make it less of a chore. Exercise gets your blood pumping around your body to your brain.

3 Keep a healthy body weight

If you follow a healthy diet and get plenty of exercise, then you should be able to keep your body weight healthy. Keep a check on your Body Mass Index (BMI) – you can work yours out by dividing your weight (in kilograms) by your height (in metres) squared. Or you can try our handy online calculator at www.yours.co.uk. A healthy BMI is between 18.5-24.9.

If your BMI is over 25 take steps to lose weight with a combination of diet and exercise.

4 Stop smoking

If you smoke, giving up is one of the most important things you can do for your brain. Smokers are twice as likely to develop dementia as non-smokers. It's thought that the chemicals in cigarette smoke causes damage to the blood vessels going to your brain. Your local GP surgery may have a free stop smoking service to help you quit.

◆ **For great weight loss advice visit www.yoursdietclub.co.uk**

5 Drink less

A little alcohol could be beneficial for your brain. For example, researchers have found that the resveratrol in red wine could help to slow down cognitive decline. But too much alcohol could have the opposite effect.

Women should aim to drink no more than two or three units per day (that's just one 175ml glass of wine), and men no more than three to four units (which equates to around one pint of beer). ➡

Protect your sight

Serious sight problems aren't inevitable as you get older, but it is completely normal for your eyesight to change.

Make sure you check your eyes regularly to pick up any problems. Check the vision in both of your eyes and in each eye separately. Look at something with detail on it such as the spine of a book or a car number plate from a particular distance away and regularly check that you can still see it. Wear your glasses if you use them, but check each eye in turn. Report anything unusual to your optometrist as soon as possible.

It's important that you don't ignore any small changes. Be aware of common signs and symptoms of age-related eye conditions. For example if you find lights dazzling and colours seem faded it could be a sign of cataracts, if the centre of your field of vision seems blurred and you're struggling to read or see faces it could suggest Age-Related Macular Degeneration (AMD).

Get your eyes checked at least every two years by an optometrist because some sight problems such as glaucoma have very few symptoms that you can pick up yourself. Don't forget sight tests are free if you're over 60 or over 40 with a family history of glaucoma.

According to the Royal National Institute of Blind People (RNIB) 50 per cent of sight loss is avoidable with simple lifestyle changes.
◆ Eat plenty of leafy green vegetables such as kale, spinach and broccoli. They are good sources of lutein and zeaxanthin, which are antioxidants thought to reduce your risk of AMD and cataracts. Omega-3 fatty acids from oily fish such as mackerel and sardines could also help to reduce inflammation in your eyes and prevent dryness. While wholegrains such as wholemeal bread, oats and brown rice could help to balance cholesterol levels and high cholesterol has been linked to an increased risk of AMD.
◆ Quit smoking: it's one of the best things you can do for your vision. Being a smoker makes you four times more likely than a non-smoker to develop AMD.
◆ Regular exercise helps to reduce your chance of developing obesity, diabetes, high blood pressure and a narrowing or hardening of the arteries, conditions that can all cause damage to the blood vessels in the eyes and brain, and potentially lead to sight loss.

Keep your heart healthy

It's easy to take your heart for granted – after all you can't see it. But it's important that you pay it some attention because coronary heart disease kills three times more women than breast cancer every year in the UK.

The good news is that looking after your heart isn't complicated. In fact three lifestyle changes could dramatically reduce your risk of heart disease (including angina and heart attack), stroke and heart failure. And if you already have heart disease these steps could help you to improve your heart health and reduce your risk of further heart problems.

Step 1: Give up smoking.

If you're a smoker, stopping smoking is the single most important thing you can do to improve your heart health. Smokers are twice as likely to have a heart attack than people who have never smoked.

As soon as you stop smoking your risk of heart disease starts to go down. Within a year of stopping your risk is reduced by about half. Most people find that quitting is easier if they have support. **Find out how to get free help from your local GP surgery or at www.smokefree.nhs.uk.**

Step 2: Eat healthily

A healthy diet could help you to protect your heart in many ways. First, it could help you to maintain a healthy weight, which is important because being overweight increases your risk of diabetes, high blood pressure and high cholesterol which all contribute to your risk of heart disease.

Aim to eat plenty of fresh fruit and vegetables, choose wholegrain carbohydrates, low-fat dairy products, lean meat and fish. It's also important to keep an eye on your salt intake. You should aim to have less than 6g a day – that's just over a teaspoonful. Check food labels and avoid typically salty foods such as crisps and takeaways. For a simple heart healthy eating plan visit **www.yoursdietclub.co.uk** and we can do all the hard work for you.

Step 3: Exercise

Making time for regular exercise could help to lower blood pressure, improve cholesterol levels and help you to lose weight. Currently less than a third of women in the UK do enough physical activity to protect their heart. Yet some experts believe that exercise may be just as effective as drugs for treating heart disease and stroke.

Aim to do 30 minutes of exercise five times a week. You don't have to do 30 minutes in one go if you find that too difficult – instead try three short 10-minute walks. You need to walk fast enough to feel warmer, breathe harder and feel your heart beat slightly faster than normal. ➡

Get stronger bones today

Improving your bone health needn't be a chore, just add a few things to your day and you could make a big difference.

Many people assume it's too late to improve their bone health once they get older. While true, it is hard to build more bone, you can certainly do a lot to preserve and strengthen what you have.

Looking after your skeleton is important because according to the National Osteoporosis Society one in two women and one in five men over the age of 50 will fracture a bone. A damaged bone might not seem like a huge problem, but breaks and fractures could have a knock on effect to other aspects your health and your independence. Do all you can to avoid a painful break by making these simple changes to your day and you should improve your bone health.

Check your weight

Regularly stepping on the scales could help you keep your weight stable. A body mass index (BMI) of 25 or more could increase your risk of osteoporosis. Being overweight affects how much Vitamin D your body can carry. For advice on losing weight visit www.yoursdietclub.co.uk

Start right

Start your day with a bone boost by including a yogurt drink that's fortified with calcium and Vitamin D with your breakfast. Try scrambled, poached or boiled eggs on toast – eggs are a good food source of Vitamin D and protein – both of which are vital for good bones.

Take a supplement

If you don't think you get enough calcium and Vitamin D it's worth taking specifically formulated bone supplement. Your local pharmacist or health food shop will be able to recommend a good one.

Go for a walk

Getting outside is important because sunlight helps your body to produce Vitamin D. If you walk to the shops and carry home your shopping you'll be getting some weight-bearing exercise too, which helps to strengthen your bones.

Calcium-rich lunch

Tuck into a tinned mackerel and spinach salad (perhaps, try tinned sardines or salmon as an alternative). Both tinned fish and green leafy vegetables contain calcium. Scatter over some walnuts for good measure too. If you're vegetarian you can increase your calcium content with a low-fat cheese salad.

Improve your balance

Good balance could help you to avoid a fall. With a chair nearby to hold on to, try balancing on one foot for as long as you can. Pulling in your stomach muscles might help make this easier. Repeat on the other foot. Tai Chi is great for balance so find out about classes in your area.

Protein-packed dinner

Grilled chicken is a healthy source of protein, serve it with fresh vegetables and have a yogurt for pudding. If you like a glass of wine choose a small one. Too much alcohol could weaken your bones.

Whittle your waist

How wide is your waistline? It's normal for it to thicken a little as you get older, but having too much fat around your middle could affect your health. The state of your waistline could be an indication of your risk of heart disease, diabetes and even some forms of cancer. If you're a woman and your waist is 32 inches (80cm) or more then your risk of these health problems is higher than someone slimmer.

The good news is that it's possible to slim your waist and reduce the amount of damaging visceral fat that causes all the problems. Visceral fat collects around your internal organs and releases inflammatory substances that are harmful to your blood vessels, liver and heart.

Tummy fat is more common post menopause because levels of protective oestrogen fall. Oestrogen causes fat to be stored on your hips, but when levels dip the fat gets stored around your middle instead.

The best way to get rid of all that bad fat is, of course, through a healthy diet and regular exercise. Visceral fat is really sensitive to physical exercise and you may find that while you might not lose weight initially your waistline will shrink. A tape measure rather than the scales is the best way of knowing if you're getting rid of your tummy fat.

Current guidelines suggest that people over 50 do at least 150 minutes (2 hours and 30 minutes) of moderate-intensity aerobic activity such as cycling, dancing or fast walking every week. To make that easier you can break it down into small 10-minute chunks. But remember, it only counts if you're being active enough to be slightly out of breath and a bit warm.

Spanish researchers have found that a Mediterranean style diet is the best way to lose tummy fat. Pack your plate with lean meat, fish, fresh fruit and vegetables, wholegrain carbohydrates, beans and pulses. Try to cut back on sugary foods and those high in saturated fat such as cakes, butter and convenience foods. ➡

How to measure your waist

Measuring your waist is simple, but it's important to remember that you aren't measuring yourself for a new pair of trousers or skirt – you may need to measure a slightly different area of your waist than you are used to. Here's how it's done:
◆ Find the top of your hipbone and the bottom of your ribs.
◆ Place your tape measure midway between these points and wrap it around your waist.
◆ Breathe out naturally.
◆ Check your measurement.

Did you know?
Because fat is less dense than muscle it takes up more space and feels softer. If you haven't gained weight but your clothes feel tight you've probably swapped some muscle for fat

Beat Tummy troubles

Most of us experience problems with digestion at some point. But as you get older you might find you have more trouble. Problems such as constipation and bloating are common in women over 50 and your digestion often becomes more sluggish as you age. Usually many of these problems can be improved with simple tweaks to your diet and lifestyle. Use our checklist to help you get on top of your tummy troubles.

Check your medication

Some medicines can cause side effects such as constipation and bloating. Speak to your GP or your pharmacist if you think your stomach issues started alongside a medical treatment. Often there is an alternative medicine that you could try or another way of treating your health problem.

Exercise

Becoming less active could contribute to constipation and bloating. Exercise is thought to rev-up a sluggish digestive system. If you're feeling bloated try going for a walk to get things moving.

Drink more

Not getting enough fluids could make constipation worse. If you experience incontinence you may be tempted to avoid drinking too much, but this could make your incontinence worse and increase your risk of constipation.

Also some blood pressure medication can make you dehydrated so try to drink plenty; at least eight glasses of water or low-sugar squash a day.

Eat healthily

A balanced diet with plenty of fruit and vegetables and wholegrain carbohydrates is great for your digestion. However, it might be wise to limit foods such as beans, cabbage, cauliflower, onions and sprouts if you're prone to wind and bloating. Wheat products, apples, pears, mushrooms and honey all encourage the growth of gas-producing bacteria in your gut so it might be worth seeing if they affect you too.

Don't forget...

Sometimes digestive problems could be a sign of something more serious. If your bowel habits change (for example you get constipation or diarrhoea and you don't usually) and the symptoms persist for more than three weeks you should speak to your GP. Also look out for blood in your stools, bloating and any unexplained weight loss. Some of these symptoms may sound trivial but it's always worth getting checked out just in case.

Beat joint pain today

Stiff, aching joints aren't inevitable as you get older but they are very common. In fact eight out of 10 people in the UK have arthritis. Dealing with pain every day is exhausting, but there are a few things you can do to help manage your aching joints and improve your pain levels each day.

Before you get up

Lie in bed and stretch your whole body. Stretch your arms up above your head, point and flex your feet, rotate your ankles and generally move your body as much as you can to mobilise your joints. The more you move your joints the less painful they should become.

Better breakfast

Have a bowl of porridge made with semi-skimmed milk or low-fat natural yogurt with fresh fruit or wholegrain cereal. Dairy products are a good source of calcium and Vitamin D, which are important if you have arthritis because you are more at risk of osteoporosis.

Fish for lunch

Try a tinned salmon sandwich or salad. Oily fish such as salmon, mackerel and sardines are full of Omega-3 fatty acids, which could help reduce inflammation in your joints.

Strengthen muscles

By making the muscles that support your joints stronger they will take the pressure off your joints and could help to ease pain. Try standing up and down slowly from your chair, walking slowly up and down the stairs, slowly scrunching a towel up in your hands or lifting light weights. Ask your GP to refer you to a physiotherapist for more help with exercises.

Spice-packed dinner

Have something full of warming spices such as cinnamon, turmeric and ginger – try a

Did you know?

Eating lots of garlic, onions and leeks could reduce your risk of arthritis of the hip, say UK scientists.

Moroccan-style tagine or a mild chicken curry. Spices are thought to contain anti-inflammatory compounds, which could help to ease your joint pain.

Go for a walk

Although moving around might be painful, if you can, it's a good idea to try and do some weight-bearing exercise. Walking is gentle on your joints and being outside could lift your mood, too, which research has found could then help to improve your perception of pain.

Before bed

Stretch your body again, giving your joints one last chance to move to help prevent stiffness over night.

Keep your feet healthy

Looking after your feet becomes really important as you get older. The skin on your feet, like the skin on your face, gets thinner with age, making it more prone to blisters, infections and problems such as corns. Foot care gets harder if you're unable to reach your feet due to joint pain or a stiff back. To keep your feet healthy follow this routine each week:

◆ Wash your feet daily and dry them thoroughly.
◆ Cut and file your nails to keep them at a comfortable length.
◆ Use a pumice stone or a foot file to remove hard skin.
◆ Apply some moisturiser to hydrate your skin and prevent it becoming cracked and sore. If you struggle to reach your feet try putting a little moisturiser on a small towel or flannel on the floor and rub your feet into it.
◆ Check for cracks and breaks in your skin and inflammation such as blisters. If you see any of these or

Foot pain

Having painful feet isn't a normal part of ageing. There are many conditions that could cause foot pain such as gout, bunions and ingrowing toenails. There is also a chance then you might have sprained or strained your foot. If you are experiencing any kind of foot pain you should speak to your GP who will be able to suggest the best ways to help.

signs of a nail fungus speak to your pharmacist or GP for advice.
◆ If you find your feet are often cold, wear bed socks at night to keep them comfortable.

If you struggle to look after your own feet speak to your GP. In some areas routine chiropody or podiatry is available on the NHS, which means if you qualify, someone will regularly check your foot health for you.

Looking after your feet is especially important if you have diabetes. Diabetes can reduce the blood supply to your feet and cause a loss of feeling known as peripheral neuropathy. This could mean that you don't notice if your foot is injured or sore. Remember to check your feet regularly for any signs of damage. Give up smoking too because it can reduce circulation even more and make peripheral neuropathy worse.

Make the most of

Once spring arrives, there are hardly enough hours in the day for gardeners. The list of tasks is almost endless but longer days and warmer weather make being outside a positive pleasure. Who could fail to enjoy pottering around the garden when accompanied by the glorious sound of birdsong and surrounded by dancing daffodils? Even better is the promise of the bounty still to come as we sow seeds, prepare the ground for vegetable crops and plan the summer flower borders. And at the end of the day, there is the luxury of soaking our aching limbs in a hot bath while contentedly reflecting on jobs well done.

12 things to do this season

◆ Check stored dahlia tubers and cut away any soft or rotting tubers with a sharp knife before planting at the end of April.

◆ Prune rose bushes on days when no frost is forecast.

◆ Remove slippery algae from paths and patios by scrubbing with diluted bleach or a proprietary cleaner.

◆ Before trimming untidy hedges, make sure that no birds are nesting within.

◆ Mulch borders with a thick layer of well-rotted organic manure or chipped bark.

◆ Give the grass its first cut in March, making sure the mower blades are set high.

◆ When the weather warms up in April, sow hardy annual seeds direct into the ground to fill any gaps in flower beds.

◆ Prune forsythia and ornamental currant bushes after flowering.

◆ In the vegetable garden, plant onion sets, carrots, beetroot and cabbages.

◆ Buy summer bedding plants ready for planting in pots and borders but keep them protected from late frosts.

◆ Check tree ties and stakes are secure to prevent rocking in windy weather.

◆ Sow sweet peas in March ready to plant out in April.

your garden... in spring!

TOP TIP: Don't throw away your grapefruit peel after breakfast! Scooped-out halves of grapefruit (or oranges) placed face down in different parts of the garden will attract slugs and snails overnight. In the morning all you need to do is gather them up and dispose of the pests.

Super shrub: Magnolia stellata

True to its name, Magnolia stellata has star-like white flowers that are borne on bare branches before the deep green leaves emerge. It forms a well-shaped bush growing to a height of 3m (10ft) and grows in alkaline as well as neutral to acid soil conditions. Magnolia stellata 'Royal Star' has double flowers and blooms later on in April.

Favourite flower: Narcissus poeticus

The pheasant's eye narcissus (Narcissus poeticus var. recurvus) doesn't bloom until late May but this graceful latecomer is well worth the wait for its perfume alone. Growing to a height of 40cm (16in), it looks particularly lovely planted in the grass round the base of a silver birch tree. Pheasant's eye is also an excellent cutting flower.

Seasonal inspiration

Magical magnolias

The gardens surrounding Caerhays Castle in Cornwall are at their stunning best in spring when they are ablaze with camellias, rhododendrons and azaleas as well as a national collection of magnolias. The 120-acre woodland gardens are English Heritage Listed Grade II and visitors can follow any of four waymarked walks around the estate or take a guided tour given by a head gardener (these need to be booked in advance). The gardens are open seven days a week from February to early June.
Email enquiries@caerhays.co.uk or call 01872 501310.

Muncaster Castle

Lakeland views

The Lake District fells form the dramatic backdrop to the gardens of Muncaster Castle in Cumbria. Boasting one of the oldest collections of rhododendrons in Europe, Muncaster also has beautiful bluebell woods in which to wander at this time of the year. From the terrace there are far-reaching views over Eskdale. Bird lovers should know that four o'clock each day is feeding time for the wild herons which gather in hungry anticipation, and also that the castle is home to The World Owl Trust.
Email info@muncaster.co.uk or call 01229 717614.

Make the most of

In the summer months the garden comes into its own as an outdoor room where all the family can relax and have fun. While there are still plenty of chores to keep the gardener busy, it's good to make time to unwind and simply enjoy being in your own bit of green and pleasant land. Few things equal the pleasure of eating outside, whether it is an evening barbecue with the neighbours or just sitting on a bench with a cup of coffee and a biscuit, watching the butterflies flit among the flowers on a sunny morning. So put those sun loungers out on the patio – it's summertime and the living is easy!

12 things to do this season

◆ Prune wisteria every three or four weeks, cutting back to one or two buds where you see whippy tendrils emerging.
◆ Support delphiniums and dahlias with stakes or pea sticks while they are still in the early stages of growth.
◆ Regularly deadhead flowers in the herbaceous border; hardy geraniums can be cut hard back to give a second flush of flowers in late summer.
◆ Cut back shrubs such as ceanothus, weigela, choisya and hebe when they have finished flowering.

◆ Rambler roses should be pruned in late summer.
◆ In July plant autumn-flowering bulbs such as hardy cyclamen, colchicums and autumn crocus.
◆ Mow the lawn twice a week and give it another feed if needed in early summer.
◆ Water pots and hanging baskets twice a day in hot weather.
◆ In the vegetable garden, harvest new potatoes, peas and beans.
◆ To prevent self-seeding, cut back lady's mantle (Alchemilla mollis) after it has flowered.
◆ In a dry spell, top up the water level in your pond.
◆ Trim conifer hedges in August.

your garden...
in summer!

Super shrub: Hydrangea paniculata

Give your garden a dash of flamboyance by planting Hydrangea paniculata 'Phantom' in a sheltered semi-shady spot. In July and August its enormous flowerheads will appear lime green in bud, opening to a creamy white before gradually fading to pink. For the best results, prune hard in early spring, cutting back to last year's side shoots. If left un-pruned, it will reach a height and spread of 2.5m (8ft). The cultivar 'Limelight' has distinctive pale green flowers.

PIC REX FEATURES

Favourite flower: Salvia nemorosa

Lovers of blue in the garden will find a sunny, well-drained spot to plant Salvia nemorosa 'Caradonna'. With its violet flower spikes borne on bright purple stems, this member of the sage family forms a compact mound with a height and spread of 45cm (18in). Its silvery green leaves are faintly aromatic and it is a magnet for bees and butterflies. If deadheaded regularly, it will flower from June to October and can withstand periods of drought. An easy-to-grow perennial, this salvia also thrives happily in a pot.

Seasonal inspiration

Roses old and new

Early summer is the perfect time to visit Mottisfont Abbey in Hampshire, said to be the loveliest rose garden in Britain. In the Seventies, the distinguished garden designer Graham Stuart Morris filled the Abbey's walled kitchen garden with the old shrub roses that he loved, underplanted with herbaceous perennials. Since then, a smaller walled garden has been planted with newer varieties of roses and the entrance courtyard features David Austin's English roses. Set on the banks of the River Test, the garden also has sweeping lawns, some fine old trees, a pleached lime walk and a parterre. During its peak in June, the garden is open in the evenings.
Visit www.nationaltrust.org.uk/mottisfont or call 01794 340757.

Newby Hall gardens

Brilliant borders

Originally planted in the Twenties and recently redesigned to give it a more contemporary colour palette, the double herbaceous border at Newby Hall gardens in Yorkshire is in brilliant bloom from June to September. The borders, backed by yew hedges, flank a grass path that runs 140m (460ft) from the house down to the River Ure. The 25-acre garden has a variety of attractions likely to appeal to visitors of all ages and tastes. There is an adventure garden and a miniature railway for children to enjoy while adults can go for a woodland walk, explore the Victorian rock garden or visit the sculpture park.
Visit www.newbyhallandgardens.com or call 0845 4504068.

Make the most of

With luck, an Indian summer will extend the time we have to enjoy being out in the garden, as well as giving us a longer window of opportunity to harvest fruit and vegetables. In the kitchen, cooks are kept busy pickling, bottling and stocking the freezer with summer's bounty – and rising to the challenge of finding a recipe for that giant marrow from the allotment! September and October are mellow months when gardeners can get ahead with a whole range of tasks before the temperature drops and the first frosts drive us reluctantly indoors. Come November, the best way to keep warm is sweeping up the leaves that drift into every corner of the dormant garden.

12 things to do this season

◆ Remove fading annuals from the flower borders; the gaps left can be planted with spring bulbs.
◆ Take hardwood cuttings of buddleia, forsythia and philadelphus to overwinter in a cold frame.
◆ Lift and divide old established clumps of herbaceous perennials and replant.
◆ Plant lily bulbs in October.
◆ In the vegetable garden, plant out spring cabbage, lettuce and broad beans.
◆ Clear fallen leaves from gutters and drains; spread a net across the garden pool to prevent leaves falling in the water.

◆ Sow parsley seeds to provide a spring crop.
◆ Plant containers with heathers, dwarf conifers and skimmias under-planted with miniature daffodils and other bulbs.
◆ Buy tulip bulbs in September but delay planting them until November to prevent tulip fire blight.
◆ Rake out dead thatch from the lawn and after the last cut give the mower its annual service.
◆ Plant container-grown and bare-rooted trees and shrubs.
◆ Protect tender plants with their own dead foliage or with straw weighted down with soil.

your garden... in autumn!

TOP TIP: If nettles are a persistent problem, sprinkle the dew-covered leaves with salt early in the morning and they will be dead by the end of the day, but take care when using salt as a weedkiller as it will damage good plants as well as the unwanted ones!

Super shrub: Euonymus alatus

The winged spindle, Euonymus alatus, thrives in most situations, but does particularly well in alkaline conditions, growing to 2.5m (8ft) with a spread of 3m (10ft). Happy in sun or partial shade, it bears yellow flowers in July and August but bursts into life in the autumn when it has purple fruit and its leaves turn from green to a vivid pinkish crimson. The dwarf cultivar 'Compactus' grows to 1m (3ft) with a spread of 3m (10ft).

PIC MASTERFILE

Favourite flower: Nerine bowdenii

The shocking pink blooms of Nerine bowdenii explode like fireworks from September through to early November. First brought to this country from South Africa by plant collector Cornish Bowden in 1903, the bulbs should be planted in late autumn in a dry, sheltered spot, ideally at the foot of a south-facing wall. Growing up to a height of 60cm (23in), nerines will flourish for several decades if left undisturbed.

Seasonal inspiration
Asters galore

Over 400 varieties of asters (also known as Michaelmas daisies) are on display in The Picton Garden near Malvern in Worcestershire (below) which opens from August to mid-October. The Picton family has specialised in growing asters since the Fifties, continuing the work of Ernest Ballard who devoted 50 years to developing these autumn-flowering daisies. In addition to asters, the garden features other autumn-flowering perennials such as Helianthus 'Lemon Queen' and Rudbeckia subtomentosa. Many of the plants grown in the garden can be bought at the adjoining Old Court Nurseries. **Email paulpicton@btinternet.com or call 01684 540416.**

Picton Garden

Breathtaking colour

Batsford Arboretum in the Cotswolds boasts the country's largest private collection of exotic as well as native trees and shrubs. Planted on a south-facing slope, the arboretum has wonderful views of the Evenlode Valley. It is open all year, except for Christmas Day, but is at its exciting best in October and November when the arboretum's collection of Japanese maples are said to be a breathtaking sight. The garden was landscaped by the first Lord Redesdale (grandfather of the famous Mitford Sisters) but is now managed by The Batsford Foundation. **Visit www.batsarb.co.uk or call 01386 701441.**

Make the most of

This is the time of year when our gardens are most often viewed through a window! From the comfort of indoors, we admire the birds feeding on the seeds and fat balls we have put out for them, the beauty of a sparkling white frost on seedheads or the effect of a low winter sun lighting up tall grasses. But even in the harshest winters there are occasional days of pale sunshine when it is possible to wrap up warm and get outside for a few hours. There is just one rule to bear in mind; avoid walking on soil or grass in freezing or waterlogged conditions as this can cause long-lasting damage.

12 things to do this season

◆ Continue hand weeding, taking extra care around any early bulbs that are pushing up through the earth.
◆ Deadhead winter-flowering pansies and violas to encourage more blooms.
◆ Take advantage of a mild frost-free spell to plant bare-rooted shrubs and trees.
◆ Rake up any autumn leaves that are still lying on the ground, but keep an eye out for hedgehogs that might be hibernating underneath.
◆ In the shed, tidy up tools, clean and oil secateurs, check to see if shears and loppers need to be sharpened.
◆ Scrub pots and plant containers clean ready for use later in the year.
◆ Order summer-flowering bulbs such as begonias, agapanthus and amaryllis.
◆ In February, prune shrubs such as buddleia and lavatera that flower after midsummer. Late-flowering clematis can also be pruned now.
◆ In the vegetable garden, cover rhubarb with a large tub, sealing any draining holes to keep the light out.
◆ Lift and divide snowdrops after flowering.
◆ Sow broad beans directly into the ground or into pots (one seed per 3in (9cm) pot) and place in an unheated greenhouse or cold frame.
◆ **Prune apple and pear trees (for beginners, courses are available from specialist orchards such as Brogdale www.brogdalecollections.co.uk tel: 01795 536250)**

your garden... in winter!

TOP TIP: Aconites can be dug up as soon as the flowers have died, but the leaves are still green. The plants should be split up and replanted as soon as possible. Alternatively, wait until the brown seed heads have formed and shake these directly on to the ground where you wish them to grow.

Seasonal inspiration

Winter wonderland

First opened to the public in 1846, Cambridge University Botanic Garden is designed for year-round interest. Its Winter Garden features bark and foliage texture with winter flower and fragrance. The latter is provided by the scented honeysuckle Lonicera x purpusii and the lily-of-the-valley perfume of Mahonia japonica. The south-facing site catches the setting sun which lights up the fiery orange stems of Salix x alba 'Chermesina'. Don't miss the garden's renowned collection of winter-flowering orchids before retreating to The Garden Café for hot coffee and a chocolate brownie. **Call 01223 336265 or visit www.botanic.cam.ac.uk**

Super shrub: Cornelian cherry

Plant a deciduous Cornelian cherry such as Cornus mas 'Golden Glory' to light up a gloomy corner with clusters of yellow flowers in late winter. Growing happily in most soils, it will further reward you with purple foliage and red berries in the autumn. It takes around 20 years to reach a height and spread of around 4m (13ft).

Colesbourne Gardens

Snowdrop drifts

Boasting 250 different varieties growing in its beautiful grounds, Colesbourne has a good claim to be England's greatest snowdrop garden. The estate has been the home of the Elwes family since 1789 but it was not until 1874 while on a visit to Turkey that the naturalist Henry John Elwes discovered the snowdrop, Galanthus elwesii, that bears his name. A yellow cultivar is called 'Carolyn Elwes' after another member of the family (which still lives at Colesbourne). The grounds are open to the public at weekends in February and March every year. **For details email info@colesbournegardens.org. uk or call 01242 870567.**

Favourite flower: Cyclamen coum

Blooming from late December right through to March, Cyclamen coum provides a joyous splash of vivid pink under the greyest of skies. The tubers prefer a well-drained soil and are best planted under trees intermingled with snowdrops and early crocuses. Growing to a height of 5cm (2in), they will naturalise and spread to form a gorgeous winter carpet. C coum 'Maurice Dryden' is a white variety for gardeners who prefer a subtler colour scheme.

Your stars for the

Astrologer, Lynne Ewart, predicts what's in store for you in 2015 and

ARIES

March 21 – April 20

The sign of the pioneer, Aries are impatient to be on their way, and usually pretty independent! You're a great leader, although you sometimes forget that others are trying to keep up, or need attention, and yet once you realise you're needed, you are a hero, a star, kind as can be. 2015 could be a year of added joy thanks to you having the inner harmony and confidence to connect well with others, to be part of a team, a community, as well as, not instead of, being the solo player. It's a year of integration that brings contentment.

Hobbies and holidays:

Above all, you are the zodiac's pioneer, and you could travel further afield than ever before, perhaps, to satisfy an ambition to see more of your world. Aries loves a hobby that has an element of speed or of physicality about it, and you thrive on a challenge, whether it's a drive on the dodgems or a fast lap in a Ferrari! 2015 favours artistic hobbies and interests and city breaks, perhaps, to places connected with your sign such as Naples or Florence. Come the autumn, though, travel and business just might intertwine in a journey with a mission in mind!

2015 signs of love and friendship:
Pisces and Leo

TAURUS

April 21 – May 21

You are the mighty oak tree who puts down roots and lets them grow and many come to you for shelter. There's a questing, surprisingly adventurous feel to your year, and the secret of success lies in looking, not outwards, but inwards. Aspects of your life that stir you to wish for change, just might shift this year, too, as you take your thoughts back in time, to a point where things worked well, and then consider making a few adjustments to your current set-up.

Family communications could improve, and a longed for reunion can finally happen in 2015.

Hobbies and holidays:

It truly soothes your soul to be growing things, and all the better if it's food, as your essential nature is all about producing what's needed. Mother Earth in all her glory fills your spirit with inner calm, so you benefit from being surrounded by greenery, whether it's having a cuppa and a cake at a garden centre or forking up the soil in your own back garden, ready for planting!

A visit to Taurus ruled Eire, a trip to the Dutch bulb fields, an away day to a spa, dancing lessons or art classes in Tuscany might delight in 2015. Holidays with an emphasis on comfort attract Taureans.

2015 signs of love and friendship:
Virgo and Libra

year ahead

suggests the pastimes and travel destinations that you'll enjoy

GEMINI
May 22 – June 21

You are the sparkly chatterbox who keeps us all in touch. Gemini, an ace communicator who must never underestimate the power of a friendly 'hello!'. There's a theme for 2015 of setting yourself achievable goals and not tripping yourself up by setting out to climb a massive mountain when reaching the summit of a small hill would be just as satisfying.

The cosmos recommends you think carefully about what fulfils you, not just what you think will suit others, especially towards the end of the year. Success will come through trusting in your own wise judgement about what's best for the long term.

Hobbies and holidays:

Variety is the spice of your life, and you love to be on the move, or else to sit and people watch, so Gemini-linked locations, such as London, Cardiff, New York and Melbourne could delight you, yet yours is the sign of the twins, and that other 'twin' can be so at home in beautiful flower-filled countryside, so long as there are wheels to keep you mobile! Geminis love gadgetry and they have to use their minds and their hands, so games that challenge your brain could appeal. Musical events and grand pageantry stir your senses, this year too.

2015 signs of love and friendship:
Leo and Scorpio

CANCER
June 22 – July 22

If you're not taking care of people, you're taking care of business and you always have a pet project on the go, or a person you need to cluck over or take chicken soup to. You're sensitive to what others feel, and sometimes feel like pulling your crab shell shutters up to protect your own soft heart. 2015 brings a time of adjustment for you, possibly in career.

It's a year for working to improve security and wellbeing. Some might consider relocating or taking on new duties in the spring. Sharing and getting the balance right at root level brings happiness.

Hobbies and holidays:

Cancer the crab is a water sign, often drawn to coastal areas; lakes, lochs and rivers. Cancerian locations include Scotland's western isles, Amsterdam and New Zealand. How about a trip on the Orient Express, or a visit to somewhere that's rich in architectural history, maybe exploring your own family tree? With your appreciation of good food, a gastronomic tour or even a cookery school experience just might titillate the taste buds in 2015!

The classic Cancerian is drawn to the world of images, so you could discover that you are a fine photographer or artist, perhaps, favouring seascapes or floral scenes.

2015 signs of love and friendship:
Sagittarius and Pisces ➡

LEO

July 23 – August 23

Life is a gift to be relished and appreciated when you are born under Leo, and you are wholehearted in all you do – no half measures. You radiate a positive, 'let's have a good time here' energy, and people gravitate to you like moths to a flame.

2015 begins with Jupiter adding wind beneath your own wings, boosting your confidence, and increasing your chances of doing well where you most hope to. Saturn's journey this year hints of extra duty, possibly around the younger members of your circle, so make sure you balance this with time for you, too.

Hobbies and holidays:

Leos can be highly active, busy bees, or they can be languid sun worshippers! They compete to win, and love to be the best they can be at whatever they tackle – so once a Leo makes a promise it's total commitment.

You tend to thrive on sunshine, and often crave a top up of winter sun, whether it's off to the Canaries, or cruising the Caribbean. This summer/autumn, Leo-ruled Italy could exert quite a tug on your romantic soul. You could enjoy sports with a social element, lavish stage spectaculars, and of course a night out with fine wines, food and friends.

2015 signs of love and friendship:
Aries and Virgo

VIRGO

August 24 – September 22

At heart, you are an analyst, someone who spots the detail that others might miss, and someone who feels great when a job has been well done. You need to be busy, either physically or mentally, although your mind is always whirring! 2015 is a year of blossoming for you, with opportunity planet Jupiter first working a little behind the scenes magic on work or fitness plans, bringing surprise support, too. Come the autumn, there's a real sense of liberation and, perhaps, a chance to spread your wings as never before. So, your cosmic message is 'never say never' Virgo!

Hobbies and holidays:

Virgo likes a journey to be laced with interesting sights and sounds, and you could enjoy a special-interest holiday to hone a skill, or a tour of an area steeped in history. Virgoans are often nimble footed, so a trip to Tango at the Tower Ballroom might tempt you! Switzerland, Croatia, and Brazil are Virgo locations. A luxury spa weekend, perhaps, with the accent on healthy living could be nicely restorative. Virgoans are great with handicrafts and you may also enjoy spare time activities spent being helpful to others. Don't underestimate the value of your input, especially over 2015!

2015 signs of love and friendship:
Sagittarius and Capricorn

LIBRA
September 23 – October 23

The sign of the scales is all about balance, and you Librans are forever striving for fairness, harmony and to achieve the right balance in everything you do. You weigh and balance and often feel undecided as favouring one option imbalances the other, hence the Libran habit of sitting on the fence and seeing both sides of every question. This same quality confers great powers of diplomacy enabling you to tread softly and therefore to walk far. 2015 is a year of branching out, which might be made possible thanks to the guidance and input of one or two experts.

Hobbies and holidays:

Countries that connect to your own star sign include Austria and Japan, and Libra also has an affinity with Portugal. Holidays should ideally involve fluffy robes and room service! If you've ever thought of learning a new language or turning teacher, 2015 is the year to do it. Indeed you might be introduced to someone whose nationality inspires you to look out your passport or to improve your linguistic skills!

Libra is often artistically or musically creative, good with colour, harmony, style and flavour, and there's rarely been a better year for you to explore your inner diva or maestro!

2015 signs of love and friendship:
Leo and Aries

SCORPIO
October 24 – Nov 22

You are a sensitive soul with great inner powers of survival, tugged by undercurrents of emotion, stirring you to do all in your power to bring light to troubled areas, to make a difference. When you listen, you are intensely focused, so people feel they can share their deepest thoughts with you and be understood. You know what it is to burn with passion for a topic dear to your heart, and you are like the phoenix who can suddenly turn life around and soar. 2015 sees you achieving a cherished ambition, with spring and autumn as your standout times.

Hobbies and holidays:

You will enjoy being away from regular routines in 2015, whether you are embracing the clear air of the Scottish Highlands, or exploring your creativity, painting poppies in southern Europe. Exotic Morocco and nippy Norway are Scorpio countries that might intrigue you!

Being on the water or near the sea does seem to be therapeutic if you're in need of a recharge, so you could be drawn to a sailing or canal barge holiday. In keeping with your very private nature, the solitary elements of fishing, reading and early morning swimming or quiet seafront walks in a warm location could appeal.

2015 signs of love and friendship:
Aquarius and Cancer ➡

SAGITTARIUS

November 23 – December 21

Life is an adventure when you are a Sagittarian, and you intend to live it fully! You are philosophical and pretty tolerant, although you disapprove of silly rules, and sometimes land in hot water for turning a blind eye to them. Your smile lights us all up though, and you tend to land on your feet – with luck finding you just when you think it's run out!

Jupiter rules your sign, and his current path is all about liberating you from what you've outgrown, and he will be bringing opportunities to enhance your security without compromising your freedom and independence.

Hobbies and holidays:

Travel is in your blood, whether it's a horse-drawn caravan in Donegal, a trip to Spain, or an outback adventure in Australia, both linked with your sign. The big wide world beckons to be explored in 2015, and you're the person to do that!

Reading and learning are always important, and if you are a typically gregarious centaur, you'll thoroughly enjoy a get-together, where there's plenty of hospitality. Sagittarians love larger-than-life theme parks and adventure movies. You are competitive and could enjoy sports, although that thirst for challenge can be satisfied through good old-fashioned, board games.

2015 signs of love and friendship:
Gemini and Capricorn

CAPRICORN

December 22 – January 20

The wonderful thing about Capricorn is that you may begin life with a slightly weighed down demeanour, but you just get better with age, eyes sparkling with humour. Saturn rules your sign, and he is currently favouring taking time out to follow lifelong ambitions which might include something you really want to learn, not necessarily for any reason other than to satisfy your own curiosity about unused skills. You might surprise those who think of you as being fairly fixed in your regular patterns, but Capricorn comes well equipped for change, and it's never too late to have an adventure!

Hobbies and holidays:

Capricorn is thrifty and has an eye for a good deal, but you also appreciate an element of privacy, so having your own accommodation, such as an apartment or villa, could feel relaxing. Places connected with your sign include Greece, India, Mexico and the Orkney Isles. Capricorn has an affinity with those dreaming spires of Oxford, too.

You are great at connecting with people, and socialising often has a purpose. Hillwalking and special interest collections often light you up, and being at one with nature's beauty is gloriously relaxing. Scenic train journeys could make your heart sing in 2015, too.

2015 signs of love and friendship:
Cancer and Scorpio

AQUARIUS
January 21 – February 18

It's not easy being an Aquarian as you see things differently to most. You dance to the tune you wrote for yourself, a true original, and your clear logic doesn't always sit sweetly with those who would tell the Emperor that his new invisible clothes are just fabulous. You'd far rather be out there being a humanitarian than pandering to popular thinking, yet you are often regarded as inspirational as you mature. 2015 shows a long-made plan swinging into action, perhaps involving a team or partnership. This could be quite a breakthrough year for shared aims and special goals.

Hobbies and holidays:

You appreciate fine minds and special talents, so journeys with a purpose, such as to attend a concert, an exhibition or to learn something new about a favourite subject could excite your travel buds in 2015!

Aquarians like sunshine, but are usually too busy to sunbathe for long, so exploring under your own steam appeals. Places connected with Aquarius include Hawaii, Sweden and Poland. Aquarian cities such as Salzburg and St Petersburg might attract you, too. Your mind is alight with bright intelligence that demands to be stimulated, so you'll enjoy chess and other games that test your knowledge.

2015 signs of love and friendship:
Taurus and Gemini

PISCES
February 19 – March 20

You are known for your sensitive, reflective nature and for your tolerant, forgiving ways, yet you are also a capable, adaptable character who lands lucky sometimes where others flop, simply because you are known as someone who won't make a drama out of a crisis.

Your intuition is strong, and compassion steers you towards healing, soothing or to charitable areas, and with ruler planet Neptune visiting Pisces over the next decade, that's more pronounced, along with creative and artistic gifts. You're less driven, more serene, and over 2015 will meet with some welcome opportunities to improve your lot in life.

Hobbies and holidays:

Pisces loves to holiday on islands, to be by water and to have solitude alternated with festivity, as those two fishes which depict your sign are forever swimming in opposite directions! You'll enjoy a city break where there's history and great architecture to set your imagination alight about times gone by, so Venice could appeal, as might a sunshine cruise. For a 2015 break, you might like Portugal, or a fun-filled trip to Florida, both Pisces linked.

Hobbies often include water-linked activities, books, music, theatre, dance, anything that transports you away from life's more mundane aspects!

2015 signs of love and friendship:
Taurus and Capricorn

Easy-peasy planters

These planters are a practical and pretty alternative to hanging baskets are perfect for smaller gardens – plus they're simple to make too!

You will need

Single-sided oilcloth
Tape measure
Rivet kit (metal) for fabrics, with post long enough to penetrate several layers of the oilcloth HammerPretty plastic coated motifs (designs from reusable shopping bags work well)
Scissors
Waterproof PVA glue or superglue
Hanging basket liner
Water-retaining gel
Multi-purpose compost

TOP TIP

These planters work just as well on balconies or over decorative fences.

1 Use a piece of oilcloth measuring 100 x 120cm (3ft 3¼in x 3ft 11in) and fold in half neatly along the shorter edge with the pattern on the outside.

2 Fold in one of the short ends by 2cm (¾in) and repeat twice more to create a seam.

3 Rivet the seam in place, starting 10cm (4in) in from the edge. To make a rivet hole in the cloth, place the plastic disc underneath and hammer the recessed end of the hole punch through the cloth.

4 Push the rivet post through the hole from underneath and tap the cap in place with the hammer. Add three more evenly spaced rivets to the seam, finishing 10cm (4in) in from the other side. Repeat steps 2-4 at the opposite short end.

5 Fold in the riveted ends, leaving enough material in the middle to allow for the width of whatever you're hanging it over. The bags should hang comfortably with the tops of the pockets just below the top of your fence or balustrade.

6 Flip the cloth over. Fold in a long side twice, including the pocket flaps, to make a 3cm (1¼in) seam. Weight the seam down to hold it as you rivet it in place.

7 Repeat with the other long side. Flip the cloth back over and you have made your 'saddle bag' planters. Repeat to make as many as you need.

8 Leave them as is, or to make them look even prettier cut out some motifs from attractive reusable shopping bags to add to sides of the saddle bags. Glue the designs onto the planters and leave to dry.

9 Take a length of hanging-basket liner and line each of the planting pockets, cutting the liner to size with scissors. It should sit just below the lip of the pocket. This will help keep the compost moist in the pockets. To conserve moisture further, add 5g (¼oz) of water-retaining gel to every 5 litres (1 gallon) of multi-purpose compost.

10 Hang the bags in their final positions. Remove plants from their pots, tease out any circling roots and position them in the pockets. Fill around with compost, and firm in. Water thoroughly.

What to plant

This plant list includes a selection that can be planted in early spring and summer. Add spring bulbs for colour and small evergreen shrubs for year-round interest.
◆ Lavender
◆ Nemesia denticulate 'Confetti'
◆ Pelargonium 'Attar of Roses'
◆ Pelargonium graveolens 'Minor'
◆ Rosemary
◆ Strawberry
◆ Sage

Small Space Big Ideas
Create your dream garden on a windowsill, wall, step, staircase, balcony, porch, or patio

This project is from Small Space, Big Ideas by Philippa Pearson (£16.99, www.dk.com/crafts)

Guilt-free birthday cakes

If baking isn't your strong point, these fabric cakes make a cute and quirky alternative – just without the calories!

You will need

Fabric 1: 46x46cm (18x18in) check
Fabric 2: 9x65cm (3½ x25½in) spot
Fabric 3: 6.5x48.5cm (2½x19in) denim
25.5x25.5cm (10x10in) red felt
Small piece of yellow felt
50cm (20in) wide ric–rac
50cm (20in) decorative tape
127.5cm (50in) square wadding
7.5cm (3in) hook-and-loop fastener (Velcro™)
Polyester stuffing
Finished size: 20cm (8in) diameter x 15.5cm (6in) high excluding candles

To make the bottom layer

1 Using a 20cm (8in) dinner plate as a template cut out two circles from fabric 1 and two matching circles from the wadding. Cut a 9x63.5cm (3½x25in) strip from the wadding (the same size as the fabric 2 strip). Spray glue or tack your fabric pieces to the wadding pieces.

TOP TIP

Make different coloured cakes for boys or girls – they make great leaving presents also!

2 Embellish the centre of the strip with decorative tape. Or you can use strips of contrasting fabrics (edge with ric-rac braid to avoid having to hem). To represent the cake's icing, tack ric-rac along the top and bottom edges of the fabric 2 strip, attaching it to the right side so the raw edges align and sewing in place along the tacking stitches. Join together the two short ends of the decorated fabric strip to form a circle and sew with a 6mm (¼in) seam allowance.

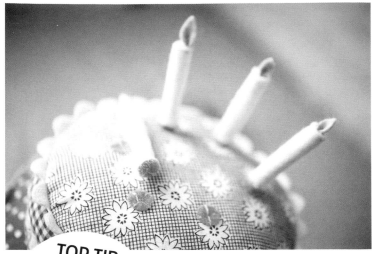

TOP TIP

Hook-and-loop fastener circles are available and these make for a neater finish when attaching the candles to the top layer of the cake.

3 Fold each circle in half and half again and finger press; open out and mark quarter folds with a pin around the edges. To find the matching quarters of the joined strip, lay it flat on your work surface, fold it in half and finger press; open it out again and mark each quarter with a pin.

4 Match up the pins on the circular strip to the pins on the circles, joining the pieces with right sides facing; pin and tack, then sew together with a 6mm (¼in) seam allowance.

5 Carefully cut a slit in the middle of the top circle and turn it through to the right side. Stuff the cake very firmly with polyester stuffing, then ladder stitch the slit together. This will be hidden when the top layer of the cake is added.

TOP TIP

Add a pretty homemade age badge... or cheat and buy one!

To make the top layer

1 Using a 15.5cm (6in) tea plate as a template cut out two circles from fabric 1 and two from the wadding. Cut a 6.5x48.5cm (2½x19in) strip from the wadding (the same size as fabric 3 strip). Spray glue or tack the fabric pieces to the wadding pieces.

2 Cut the hook-and-loop fastener into eight 5mm (³⁄₁₆in) squares, and separate the hooks from the loops. Working on the right side of one of the fabric circles, arrange the hook squares in a circle, with one in the middle, and sew in place. Set aside the loop squares to attach to the bottom of the fabric candles later.

3 Make the top layer of the cake in exactly the same way as the bottom layer, except this time sew the ric-rac in the top seam only and cut the turning/stuffing slit on the bottom of the cake (that is the side that does not have the fastener tape attached).

4 Once stuffed place the top layer of cake on top of the bottom layer so that it is centred to cover the ladder stitch seams. Join the two cake layers together with ladder stitch using a strong, doubled thread. You may need to sew round the cake twice.

To make the candles

1 Cut pieces of red felt 5x10cm (2x4in). Starting at one short edge, roll up each piece of felt into a tube and stitch to hold in place.

2 Cut out a yellow felt 'flame' for each candle and fold in half. Tuck a flame into the middle of the candle and secure with a stitch. Sew the loop squares to the bottom of the candles. All that remains is to attach the candles on to the top of the cake by matching up the hook-and-loop squares.

This project is from Celebrate with a Stitch by Mandy Shaw (£14.99, published by David & Charles, 0844 880 5851 www.stitchcraftcreate.co.uk)

Handmade notebook

These unique journals make a thoughtful gift for loved ones

You will need

Bone folder (or the blunt side of a dinner knife)
Craft knife
Pencil
Metal ruler
Cutting mat
Sewing needle
6 x sheets of heavy A3 white or cream paper
1 x sheet of decorative paper
White cotton sewing thread

1 Making sure that the grain is running vertically fold each piece of white or cream A3 paper in half lengthways and smooth the crease with the bone folder (or the back of a knife). Again, fold each sheet of paper in half lengthways, and then fold again lengthways, each time firmly smoothing down the creases. Assemble the folded paper in a pile of 'stacks'.

2 To make the cover, fold the decorative paper in half along its width and press the crease down with the bone folder. Next fold the paper lengthways and smooth down the crease.

3 Open the cover and draw a line down this crease. Measure the height of the pile of paper stacks (the spines), then measure the same distance to the right side of the crease. Draw a line. Use the ruler and the bone folder to crease the cover along the second pencil line to create your spine.

4 Measure the height of the cover, and divide this distance into five equal sections. Mark each section on the spine, and then use a craft knife to cut a slit through each line.

5 Use the ruler to draw lines on the pile of paper stacks to correspond with the slits in the cover. Prick a needle through each mark and you should have four evenly spaced holes in each paper segment. In pencil mark these A, B, C, D and do the same with the slits you made in your cover.

6 With one stack on top of the cover, push the needle through the first hole (hole A) and first slit (slit A) from the inside. Pass the thread around the top of the spine and tie a knot.

7 Pass the needle through hole B from the inside and out through slit B. Run the thread along the spine and push the needle in through slit C and hole C to the inside.

8 Push the needle out through hole D and slit D. Looping the thread around the bottom of the spine, push the needle through just hole D again. Tighten the thread.

9 Add the next stack. Pass the needle through the first hole of the new stack (hole 2D) to the inside, then through hole 2C and slit C to the outside. Repeat for 2B and 2A.

10 Add a new stack and continue, securing pages and adding stacks. After the last stack, pass the needle around the top of the journal, and below one of the stitches. Knot on the inside.

11 Fold the decorative paper back over the stack and smooth it down, creasing the fold with your finger. Now fold the paper under again to form the jacket. Repeat for the other side.

12 Cut through the tops of the pages of the first stack. Repeat for all the other stacks.

TOP TIP

Use wallpaper offcuts or quality wrapping paper for the covers

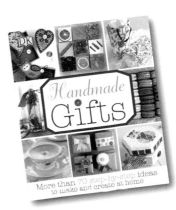

This project is from Handmade Gifts (£16.99, published by DK, www.dk.com/crafts)

Christmas tree bunting

Bunting is perfect for Christmas and this garland looks gorgeous hung on the tree or along the fireplace

You will need

Two pieces of white linen each measuring 15.5x40.5cm (6x16in)
Lightweight iron-on interfacing measuring 15.5x46cm (6x18in)
60cm (23⅝in) of 1.3cm (½in) wide ribbon
Four small red bells
Red coton à broder (high quality embroidery thread)
Clips for hanging
Finished size: 60x10cm (23⅝x4in)

1 Make a simple triangle shaped template from paper or card and cut out (the top of the triangle should be approx. 6cm (2½in). Use the card template to mark out five flags on to one piece of your linen fabric using a washable pen (remembering to add at least 1cm (½in) seam allowance on all three sides) and leave 5cm (2in) in between each flag.

2 Use a scanner or photocopier to enlarge each embroidery designs (above right) by 200%. Then trace one of the five Christmas designs in the centre of each flag; don't worry if the designs go over the edge slightly. Iron the lightweight interfacing to the back of the fabric.

TOP TIP
The ribbon lengths left at either end of the garland are long enough to allow you to tie the bunting to the tree if you're not using clips.

3 Backstitch the Christmas motif outlines using the red thread and then add the finer details. Work a circle of star stitches for the Christmas wreath adding a cluster of three French knot 'berries' in between. Add lines of running stitch to the ribbon tails. Add a French knot eye to the robin. Work a French knot bauble at the end of each of the tree's branches and add a star stitch to the top of the tree. Work a mass of French knots for the angel's hair and a gentle curve of star stitches between the hands for the garland.

4 For the snowman, work French knots for his eyes and nose and a star stitch nose. Add a star stitch bobble to the top of his hat and running stitch borders to the hatband. To complete his scarf, work French knots to the tops of the scarf fringing. Add a scattering of star stitches to the background of each flag to finish the embroidery.

5 Once the embroidery is complete, turn the fabric over and use your card template to mark the flags over the embroidered designs. Place the embroidered fabric on top of the second piece of linen fabric, right sides together, and machine stitch over the marked lines, leaving the tops of the flags open. Cut out around the flags, trim the seams, and turn right sides out.

6 Sew a running stitch border around the inside edge of each of the completed flags.

7 Lay the ribbon right side down on your work surface. Starting 10cm (4in) from the left-hand edge, place a flag with the embroidered side facing down so that the unstitched top aligns with the centre line of the ribbon. Leaving a 2.5cm (1in) gap, pin the second flag in place on to the ribbon as before. Repeat to pin the remaining flags in place, ending with a 10cm (4in) length of ribbon or tape at the right-hand side.

8 Using a thread that matches the ribbon, machine stitch the flags in place close to the edge of the ribbon. Fold the ribbon over to the back of the flags and slip stitch by hand. Sew together the edges of the ribbon lengths at either end with a machine or hand running stitch. Thread a clip on at each end of the ribbon; fold over the ribbon ends and sew in place to secure. Sew on the jingle bells between each flag to finish.

TOP TIP
It's easier to embroider the small flags as a larger piece of work, and once finished cut them to the correct size.

This project is from Celebrate with a Stitch by Mandy Shaw (£14.99, published by David & Charles, 0844 880 5851 www.stitchcraftcreate.co.uk)

Facts and figures

Here are some handy conversion tables for cooks

Dry weight

IMPERIAL	METRIC
½ oz	15 g
1 oz	25 g
2 oz	50 g
3 oz	75 g
4 oz	110 g
5 oz	150 g
6 oz	175 g
7 oz	200 g
8 oz	225 g
9 oz	250 g
10 oz	275 g
11 oz	300 g
12 oz	350 g
13 oz	375 g
14 oz	400 g
15 oz	425 g
1 lb	450 g
1 lb 2 oz	500 g
1 ½ lb	680 g
1lb 10oz	750 g
2 lb	900 g

Liquid

IMPERIAL	METRIC
½ fl oz	15 ml
1 fl oz	30 ml
2 fl oz	60 ml
3 fl oz	90 ml
4 fl oz	125 ml
5 fl oz (¼ pint)	150 ml
6 fl oz	175 ml
8 fl oz	225 ml
10 fl oz (¼ pint)	300 ml
12 fl oz	350 ml
16 fl oz	450 ml
18 fl oz	500 ml
20 fl oz (1 pint)	600 ml
1 ½ pints	900 ml
1 ¾ pints	1 litre
2 pints	1.25 litres
2 ½ pints	1.5 litres
3 ½ pints	2 litres

*Quantities aren't exact but have been calculated to give proportional measurements

Oven temperatures

°C	°C with fan	°F	Gas Mark
110	90	225	¼
120/130	100/110	250	½
140	120	275	1
150	130	300	2
160/170	140/150	325	3
180	160	350	4
190	170	375	5
200	180	400	6
220	200	425	7
230	210	450	8
240	220	475	9

Other equivalents

Dash	$1/16$ teaspoon
Pinch	$1/8$ teaspoon
1 tablespoon	3 teaspoons
$1/8$ cup	2 tablespoons
$1/4$ cup	4 tablespoons
$1/3$ cup	5 tablespoons plus 1 teaspoon
$1/2$ cup	8 tablespoons
$3/4$ cup	12 tablespoons
1 cup	16 tablespoons or 8 fl oz

Cake tin sizes

Round tin		Square tin	
6 inches	15 cm	5 inch	13 cm
8 inches	20 cm	7 inch	18 cm
9 inches	23 cm	8 inches	20 cm
11 inches	28 cm	10 inches	25.5 cm

Healthy eating

Guideline daily amounts for adults

Women should aim to eat no more than 2,000 kcal each day (men 2,500 kcal)
– spaced across the day this would be:
400 kcal at breakfast (including drinks)
600 kcal at lunch (including drinks)
600kcal for your evening meal (including drinks)
no more than 400 kcal for healthy snacks

The guidelines (below) will help you identify if a product is high in fat, saturated fat, salt or sugar or not.

Total fat
High = more than 20g of fat per 100g
Low = 3g of fat or less per 100g
Saturated fat
High = more than 5g of saturated fat per 100g
Low = 1.5g of saturated fat or less per 100g
Sugars
High = more than 15g of total sugars per 100g
Low = 5g of total sugars or less per 100g
Salt
High = more than 1.5g of salt per 100g (or 0.6g sodium)
Low = 0.3g of salt or less per 100g (or 0.1g sodium)

How to get your five a day

We all know that for optimum health we should eat five portions of fruit and veg a day
– but what is a portion?

A portion of fruit (80g) is roughly equivalent to:
A slice of melon
Half a grapefruit.
1 medium size fruit, for example, an apple.
2 small size fruits, such as plums or satsumas.

A portion of dried fruit (30g) is roughly equivalent to:
A heaped tablespoon of dried fruit

A portion of vegetables (80g) is roughly equivalent to:
3 heaped tablespoons of peas, beans or pulses.
2 broccoli spears.
A dessert bowl of salad.

**For more advice on healthy eating
visit either www.nhs.uk/livewell
or www.nhs.uk/Change4Life**

Notable dates 2015

New Year's Day (Bank Holiday)	Thursday January 1
Epiphany	Tuesday January 6
Burns' Night	Sunday January 25
Valentine's Day	Saturday February 14
Shrove Tuesday (Pancake Day)	Tuesday February 17
Ash Wednesday	Wednesday February 18
Chinese New Year (Year of the Sheep)	Thursday February 19
St David's Day	Sunday March 1
Commonwealth Day	Monday March 9
Mothering Sunday	Sunday March 15
St Patrick's Day (Bank Holiday N. Ireland/Eire)	Tuesday March 17
British Summer Time begins (clocks go forward)	Sunday March 29
Palm Sunday	Sunday March 29
Good Friday (Bank Holiday)	Friday April 3
Easter Day	Sunday April 5
Easter Monday (Bank Holiday)	Monday April 6
St George's Day	Thursday April 23
May Day (Bank Holiday)	Monday May 4
Ascension Day	Thursday May 14
Whitsun (Bank Holiday)	Monday May 25
Fathers' Day	Sunday June 21
Summer Solstice (Longest day)	Sunday June 21
Wimbledon Tennis Tournament begins	Monday June 29
Armed Forces Day	Saturday June 27
First Day of Ramadan (Islam)	Thursday June 18
American Independence Day	Saturday July 4
Battle of the Boyne (Holiday N. Ireland)	Monday July 13
St Swithun's Day	Wednesday July 15
Bank Holiday (Scotland / Eire)	Monday August 3
August Bank Holiday	Monday August 31
Jewish New Year	Monday September 14
Trafalgar Day	Wednesday October 21
British Summer Time ends (clocks go back)	Sunday October 25
Bank Holiday (Eire)	Monday October 26
Hallowe'en	Saturday October 31
Guy Fawkes' Night	Thursday November 5
Remembrance Sunday	Sunday November 8
Diwali (Hindu Festival of lights)	Wednesday November 11
First Sunday in Advent	Sunday November 29
St Andrew's Day	Monday November 30
Winter Solstice (Shortest day)	Tuesday December 22
Christmas Day (Bank Holiday)	Friday December 25
Boxing Day (Bank Holiday)	Saturday December 26
New Year's Eve/Hogmanay	Thursday December 31

Sunrise & sunset times

	SUNRISE	SUNSET
Jan 1	8:06 am	4:02 pm
Feb 1	7:39 am	4:49 pm
Mar 1	6:46 am	5:40 pm
April 1	6:37 am	7:33 pm
May 1	5:33 am	8:23 pm
June 1	4:49 am	9:08 pm
July 1	4:47 am	9:21 pm
Aug 1	5:24 am	8:49 pm
Sept 1	6:12 am	7:48 pm
Oct 1	7:00 am	6:39 pm
Nov 1	6:53 am	4:34 pm
Dec 1	7:43 am	3:55 pm

SOURCE: WWW.TIMEANDDATE.COM

Weather: UK averages

Number of hours of sunshine

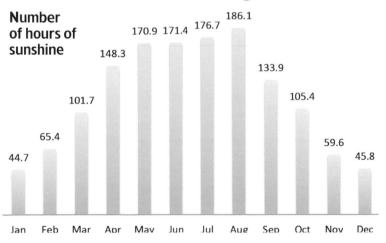

Jan 44.7, Feb 65.4, Mar 101.7, Apr 148.3, May 170.9, Jun 171.4, Jul 176.7, Aug 186.1, Sep 133.9, Oct 105.4, Nov 59.6, Dec 45.8

Rainfall in Millimetres

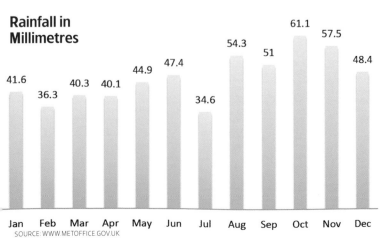

Jan 41.6, Feb 36.3, Mar 40.3, Apr 40.1, May 44.9, Jun 47.4, Jul 34.6, Aug 54.3, Sep 51, Oct 61.1, Nov 57.5, Dec 48.4

SOURCE: WWW.METOFFICE.GOV.UK

Anniversaries

1 PAPER
2 COTTON
3 LEATHER
4 BOOKS
5 WOOD
6 IRON
7 WOOL
8 BRONZE
9 COPPER
10 TIN
11 STEEL
12 SILK
13 LACE
14 IVORY
15 CRYSTAL
20 CHINA
25 SILVER
30 PEARL
35 CORAL
40 RUBY
45 SAPPHIRE
50 GOLDEN
55 EMERALD
60 DIAMOND
65 BLUE SAPPHIRE
70 PLATINUM

Birthstones

Month	Stone
January	Garnet
February	Amethyst
March	Aquamarine
April	Diamond
May	Emerald
June	Pearl
July	Ruby
August	Peridot
September	Sapphire
October	Opal
November	Topaz
December	Turquoise

2015 year-to-view calendar

JANUARY						
M		5	12	19	26	
Tu		6	13	20	27	
W		7	14	21	28	
Th	1	8	15	22	29	
F	2	9	16	23	30	
Sa	3	10	17	24	31	
Su	4	11	18	25		

FEBRUARY						
M		2	9	16	23	
Tu		3	10	17	24	
W		4	11	18	25	
Th		5	12	19	26	
F		6	13	20	27	
Sa		7	14	21	28	
Su	1	8	15	22		

MARCH						
M		2	9	16	23	30
Tu		3	10	17	24	31
W		4	11	18	25	
Th		5	12	19	26	
F		6	13	20	27	
Sa		7	14	21	28	
Su	1	8	15	22	29	

APRIL						
M		6	13	20	27	
Tu		7	14	21	28	
W	1	8	15	22	29	
Th	2	9	16	23	30	
F	3	10	17	24		
Sa	4	11	18	25		
Su	5	12	19	26		

MAY						
M		4	11	18	25	
Tu		5	12	19	26	
W		6	13	20	27	
Th		7	14	21	28	
F	1	8	15	22	29	
Sa	2	9	16	23	30	
Su	3	10	17	24	31	

JUNE						
M	1	8	15	22	29	
Tu	2	9	16	23	30	
W	3	10	17	24		
Th	4	11	18	25		
F	5	12	19	26		
Sa	6	13	20	27		
Su	7	14	21	28		

JULY						
M		6	13	20	27	
Tu		7	14	21	28	
W	1	8	15	22	29	
Th	2	9	16	23	30	
F	3	10	17	24	31	
Sa	4	11	18	25		
Su	5	12	19	26		

AUGUST						
M		3	10	17	24	31
Tu		4	11	18	25	
W		5	12	19	26	
Th		6	13	20	27	
F		7	14	21	28	
Sa	1	8	15	22	29	
Su	2	9	16	23	30	

SEPTEMBER						
M		7	14	21	28	
Tu	1	8	15	22	29	
W	2	9	16	23	30	
Th	3	10	17	24		
F	4	11	18	25		
Sa	5	12	19	26		
Su	6	13	20	27		

OCTOBER						
M		5	12	19	26	
Tu		6	13	20	27	
W		7	14	21	28	
Th	1	8	15	22	29	
F	2	9	16	23	30	
Sa	3	10	17	24	31	
Su	4	11	18	25		

NOVEMBER						
M		2	9	16	23	30
Tu		3	10	17	24	
W		4	11	18	25	
Th		5	12	19	26	
F		6	13	20	27	
Sa		7	14	21	28	
Su	1	8	15	22	29	

DECEMBER						
M		7	14	21	28	
Tu	1	8	15	22	29	
W	2	9	16	23	30	
Th	3	10	17	24	31	
F	4	11	18	25		
Sa	5	12	19	26		
Su	6	13	20	27		

DIARY 2015

29	Monday
30	Tuesday
31	Wednesday
1	Thursday
2	Friday
3	Saturday
4	Sunday

Seems like only yesterday

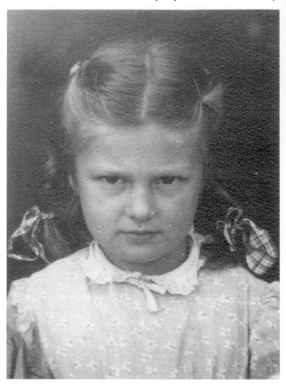

Down our street

I think you can tell from my expression in this photo what I felt about being at infant school! Born in 1943, I grew up in a terraced house that had no bathroom, only a wash-house with a cold water tap. Baths were taken in a tin bath in water that had been heated up in saucepans. Our outside toilet was shared with neighbours.

The street was our favourite playground and children played happily together with occasional squabbles. Boisterous games were tolerated by adults but I do remember one lady threatening to throw a bucket of water over us – and woe betide any child who damaged precious vegetables growing in the gardens!

We wandered freely with no one concerned about our safety. Parents knew we would always return for mealtimes! Our treat was the Saturday morning cinema. The programme always began with the Ovaltineys song, followed by a cartoon and finally a feature film, often starring Roy Rogers or Gene Autry. The morning ended with a visit to the fish and chip shop for 'threepennorth' of chips and batter bits.

Everyone was friendly, families stayed close and neighbours helped each other. The only signs of war were the gas masks hanging up in a cupboard (just in case) and German planes flying overhead, heading for Coventry or Birmingham.

Mrs Patricia Jackson, Bewdley, Worcs

It's a fact

A mousey marriage: Wayne Anthony Allwine, who was the voice of Mickey Mouse for 32 years, got married to Russi Taylor, who played Minnie, in 1991. The two remained happily married until his death in 2009.

Turn back time tips

A handful of walnuts every day could reduce your risk of heart disease by 55 per cent and your risk of cancer by 40 per cent. Walnuts are a great source of heart-healthy mono-unsaturated fats.

Great days out

Sunday Creative Workshops

Kenwood House, Hampstead, Jan 4
Need to get out after the post-Christmas slump? Take the grandchildren for one last treat before school starts, at this arts and crafts afternoon. The first of these family-friendly workshops takes place this Sunday; however there are additional dates at the beginning of February and March if you can't quite brave going out yet. All activities are free; you just need to turn up and get stuck in! 12pm-4pm. **Call 0208 348 1286 or visit www.english-heritage.org.uk/kenwood**

It made me laugh

I needed a new dressing gown, and found one at a jumble sale for 10p. Unfortunately, it didn't fit so I gave it to the charity shop. A few days later a friend phoned in great excitement: "I've got you a dressing gown from the charity shop and it was only £2.25!" I didn't have the heart to tell her it was the one I'd originally bought for 10p!　　**J Walsh, Bolton, Lancashire**

Recipe of the week

Pan Roasted Chicken with Cranberry and Mushroom Sauce

Serves: 4
Preparation time: 10 minutes
Cooking time: 25 minutes

4 boneless chicken breasts
2 tbsp extra virgin olive oil
Salt and pepper
3-4 tbsp plain flour
1 tbsp butter
2 shallots, peeled and sliced
250g (8oz) chestnut mushrooms
Brandy for deglazing the pan
150g (5oz) cranberry sauce
50g (2oz) dried cranberries
300ml (1/2pt) chicken stock
3-4 tbsp double cream or crème fraîche

1 Heat oil in a large frying pan over medium high heat. Season the chicken to taste, then coat with flour and shake off excess. Cook the chicken until golden brown, then turn and cook for an additional 5-6 minutes, or until the chicken is cooked through. Remove the chicken from the pan and leave to rest.
2 Add a drizzle more oil and the butter to the pan. Add the shallots and mushrooms and cook for 5-6 minutes, stirring occasionally until the mushrooms are golden brown. Add a splash of brandy to deglaze the pan.
3 Add the chicken stock and cranberry sauce, stir, then return the chicken to the pan and simmer for 5 minutes. Stir in the cranberries, cream or crème fraîche and serve with rice or mashed potatoes.
© www.oceanspray.co.uk

5 Monday

6 Tuesday

7 Wednesday

8 Thursday

9 Friday

10 Saturday

11 Sunday

Seems like only yesterday

A WAAF in wartime

I grew up in Hemel Hempstead and at the age of 14 had to leave school and find a job. The John Dickinson papermaking and stationery factory was the main source of employment locally. I was offered a desk job in the envelope department checking the output of the machines. The hours were from eight in the morning to six o'clock in the evening with an hour for lunch. On Saturdays I worked from eight to 12:30.

The Second World War broke out two years after I'd started work and it changed many lives. Most of the men in the factory were called up and I changed my job to running an envelope machine which meant earning more money. While I was at John Dickinson I met my future husband and as he had gone into the Navy I decided to join the WAAF. My first posting was to Blackpool where I spent my first Christmas away from home. I was billeted in what had been a holiday guesthouse and shared a bedroom with three other girls. It was a case of learning to adapt to a different way of life as well as embarking on a new career. In a large building (I think it was called Olympia) we sat at tables covered with all the trappings of wireless telegraphy. I remember Morse code to this day. Not so pleasant were the church parades on the sea front in freezing cold weather, but I enjoyed the whole experience.

Mrs Ida Jackson, Doncaster

It's a fact

Giraffes are the tallest animals on the planet, with their neck alone reaching an average length of 2.4m long – yet amazingly they have the same number of bones in their necks as humans: a mere seven!

Turn back time tips

Most of us religiously apply a good face cream morning and night and will even slap on a body lotion, but what about that bit in the middle? If you don't want to buy a separate neck cream simply sweep your face cream down a bit further and your body cream up a bit more for a wrinkle-busting double whammy.

Great days out

PIC: NATIONAL TRUST AND ANDREAS VON EINSIEDEL

Bath Assembly Rooms

Bennett Street, Bath, Somerset
The Assembly Rooms were at the heart of fashionable Georgian society, and the perfect entertainment venue. Brand new in 1771, they were described as 'the most noble and elegant of any in the kingdom'. Fear not, though, intrepid travellers, you will not be expected to dance all afternoon. There's a café – hurrah! Rooms, café and shop open daily. **Call 01225 477173 or visit www.nationaltrust.org.uk/bath-assembly-rooms**

It made me laugh

Did you hear about the man who lost his left arm and left leg in a car accident? He's all right now.
Tracy Davidson, Stratford-on-Avon, Warwickshire

Recipe of the week

Zesty Lemon and Lime Cheesecake

Serves: 4
Preparation time: 10 minutes
Setting time: 2 hours

500g (1lb) Alpro Lemon & Lime yogurt alternative
3 tbsp elderflower cordial
1 tbsp agar flakes
50g (2oz) toasted hazelnuts
75g (3oz) oatcakes
2 tbsp maple flavoured agave syrup
50ml (2floz) rapeseed oil
Fresh elderflowers (optional)

1 Add the yogurt alternative, elderflower cordial and agar flakes to a small pan and warm over medium heat for 5 minutes, whisking to dissolve the flakes.
2 Using a rolling pin, crush the hazelnuts and oatcakes until you have medium to fine crumbs. Add the syrup and rapeseed oil to the mixture and stir. Scoop the mixture into the base of 4 glasses.
3 Pour the yogurt mixture over the bases and place in the fridge to set. Decorate with fresh elderflowers to serve.
Top tip: Any regular lemon and lime flavoured yogurt works just as well
© www.alpro.com/uk

12 Monday

13 Tuesday

14 Wednesday

15 Thursday

16 Friday

17 Saturday

18 Sunday

Seems like only yesterday

Sisters Elizabeth, Anna and Jenny

Brownies had fun!

I have happy memories of being a Brownie in the Fifties when we had fun and also learned a lot. The uniform was very different from today. We wore brown dresses, buckle belts, woollen hats or berets and dark-coloured shoes. Before we were enrolled we had to know the Brownie promise, law and motto as well as how to salute and fold the tie correctly.

The evening started with each team of six dancing round the toadstool and singing their song. (I was a Pixie.) Our subs, six halfpennies or three pennies, were placed in front of us before Brown Owl inspected us to make sure our shoes were clean and our ties tied properly. We were then told which team was the best and where we needed to make improvements.

After the inspection we played games and did badge work. The golden bar badge was for knowledge of road safety, the national anthem and our flag. The golden hand badge was for nature study, compass reading, knitting and semaphore. We also gained cooking and ironing badges. The evening ended with singing and Brownie bells.

Once a month we had church parades. Our pack holidays were generally spent in church halls although I spent one at a boys' boarding school just outside Bristol. When we were at camp we went for walks, did craft work and played games. We also enjoyed midnight feasts!

Mrs Jenny Broe, Henbury, Bristol

It's a fact

Chaffinches are a common garden companion, but your neighbourhood bird might have something unique to your area – a regional accent! Scientists recently discovered that the males develop different songs depending on where they live, and were able to pinpoint where an individual was raised from its specific 'accent'.

Turn back time tips

Swap a sugary drink for a glass of water and you could prevent a post-menopausal belly bulge. Sugary drinks affect your energy levels and could lead to extra snacking.

Great days out

Blenheim Palace

Woodstock, Oxfordshire
It might be home to the 11th Duke and Duchess of Marlborough, but we love Blenheim because it's the birthplace of Winston Churchill. During 2015 the palace will host a special exhibition to commemorate the 50th anniversary of his death. Time your visit right and you might even get to eat in the Orangery. It's open once a month for Sunday lunch. **Call 0800 849 6500 or visit www.blenheimpalace.com**

It made me laugh

My late mum loved doing crosswords, but she was never really very good at them. I remember one particular time when the clue was "A yellow fruit, 6 letters". My mum's answer? Orange!
Linda Spooner, Worksop, Nottinghamshire

Recipe of the week

Cheese and Potato Parcels

Makes 12
Preparation time: 30 minutes
Cooking time: 30 minutes

200g (7oz) sweet potato, peeled, sliced and parboiled
200g (7oz) King Edward potato, peeled, sliced and parboiled
1 red onion, thinly sliced
2 tbsp olive oil
250g (8oz) ricotta
250g (8oz) strong Cheddar cheese, grated
200g (7oz) Greek-style natural yogurt
100g (3½oz) onion marmalade
1 egg
Salt and pepper
2 x 500g packs readymade short crust pastry
Sesame seeds, poppy seeds and egg wash (1 beaten egg plus 1 tbsp milk)

1 Preheat the oven to 200°C/400°F/Gas Mark 6, line a baking tray with parchment paper, and fry the onion in oil until translucent.
2 Mix the cooled potatoes, ricotta, cheese, yogurt, marmalade and egg and season to taste.
3 Roll out a pastry block on a floured surface to a rectangle 2cm (1in) thick, and cut into 6 even squares. Place a large spoonful of potato mixture in the centre of each. Brush water around the edges with a pastry brush, then take each corner of the pastry and bring it to the middle, pinching at the top to seal. Brush with egg wash completely all around and sprinkle with sesame or poppy seeds
4 Bake for 25-30 minutes until golden and cooked through. Serve warm or cold.
© www.rachelsorganic.co.uk

19	Monday

20	Tuesday

21	Wednesday

22	Thursday

23	Friday

24	Saturday

25	Sunday

Seems like only yesterday

Barney's day out

This is me with our cocker spaniel, Barney, who was very much part of our household. I got him from an old lady who owned the nearby sweet shop. Barney was the 'left-out' pup that no one wanted, so he came to live with us when he was just a few months old.

I loved him lots and would spend hours grooming him and combing his 'feathers'. He was so patient with us kids and would let us do anything with him. He'd sit in the wheelbarrow while we did a trip around the garden – until he could bear my wobbly steering no longer and jumped out. He even let my mum peg his ears back to stop them drooping into his food at mealtimes.

I remember, one summer, when the whole family went for a ride to Horsham Pass. As we were eating our picnic, Barney caught sight of a sheep. Suddenly, our quiet, docile, obedient spaniel tugged on his lead and cavorted across the heather with all of us in his wake. We did catch him in the end, but that was the end of our picnic. We bundled him back in the car and hurriedly drove away in case the farmer had seen what had happened. Luckily, no harm was done, but we never took Barney for a picnic there again!

Miss Gill Hughes, Northwich, Cheshire

It made me laugh

My son's girlfriend finished with him after she found he was being unfaithful to her and I couldn't blame her. She returned some post of his and I had to smile when I saw what she had written on the front of the envelope – 'Second Class Male'!

Jeena Sumner, Muswell Hill, London

It's a fact

Before the invention of nylon bristles in the late Thirties, toothbrushes actually enabled decay and disease. Up until that time, the bristles where made from hog hair and their hollow shafts had an unpleasant habit of retaining bacteria.

Turn back time tips

Avoid matching accessories as they can quickly date an outfit. Stick to bold items and save your finer jewellery for special occasions. Don't go overboard with accessories though, stick to one statement piece or a couple of pieces that complement each other rather than match.

Great days out

PIC: NITB

Ulster Folk & Transport Museum

Cultra, Northern Ireland
From moving pictures to basket weaving, patchwork quilts, print shops and old-fashioned leatherwork, this museum has it covered. It's fascinating to learn about the industrial and country folk of 100 years ago, and the guides in costume will put you at ease. Electric trams and horse-drawn carriages await in the Transport Museum. Time to put your feet up instead? Pop into the silent Picture House. **Call 0289 042 8428 or visit www.nmni.com.uftm**

Recipe of the week

Chocolate, Beetroot and Chilli Brownies

Makes: 16 brownies
Preparation time: 10–15 minutes
Cooking time: 30 minutes

250g (8oz) dark chocolate (70% cocoa solids)
100g (3^1/2oz) butter, plus extra for greasing
250g (8oz) cooked beetroot, drained
3 eggs
250g (8oz) light brown sugar
150g (5oz) ground almonds
2 tbsp cocoa powder
1 tbsp baking powder
1 tbsp vanilla extract
1 tbsp cayenne pepper powder (optional)
Icing sugar, to dust

1 Preheat the oven to 180°C/350°F/Gas Mark 4. Grease a 23cm (10in) square baking tin with a little butter and line with baking paper.
2 Break the chocolate into squares. Set over a pan of simmering water in a heatproof bowl to gently melt, stirring.
3 Blend the beetroot to a purée, add the melted chocolate, butter and eggs, then blend again. Finally add the sugar, almonds, cocoa, baking powder and cayenne (if using) and process to a smooth batter.
4 Pour into the prepared tin and bake for 30 minutes until the top is set and the brownie pulls away from the sides. Don't worry if it seems soft, as it will firm up on cooling. Remove from the oven, place on a cooling rack and let cool in the tin. Ease the brownie from the tin, cut into squares, and dust with a little icing sugar.

© www.lovebeetroot.co.uk

26 Monday

27 Tuesday

28 Wednesday

29 Thursday

30 Friday

31 Saturday

1 Sunday

Seems like only yesterday

Stocking the larder

When I was growing up in Woking, shopping for food was very different from today. Many items were delivered – milk from Scotcher's Farm was left on our doorstep every morning and Pullinger's Bakery delivered bread twice a week. The butcher, Lewis's, also delivered twice a week. A large van from Roakes Farm brought vegetables and fruit in season. The van had an aisle down the middle so customers could enter and decide what to buy.

Once a week my mother went to Sainsbury's to buy butter, margarine, lard, cheese and bacon. Chunks of butter, margarine or lard were cut from large slabs and patted into small rectangles using two wooden paddles. The finished blocks were wrapped in greaseproof paper. A large barrel-shaped Cheddar cheese was placed on a marble slab and cut into segments of the required weight by a long thin stainless steel wire with a wooden handle at each end.

We kept our own chickens which provided all the eggs we needed (as well as a meal for special occasions such as Christmas). They were fed on fruit and vegetable peel and any left-over food cooked up with oatmeal. Like many other households in the Fifties, we grew our own vegetables and fruit. Apples and pears that my mother hadn't turned into jam or preserved were wrapped in newspaper and stored in the garden shed.

John Brook, Christchurch, Dorset

It's a fact

We all know the body is made up of tiny atoms, but it can be hard to imagine quite how small these actually are – and knowing the numbers involved doesn't make it any easier! An adult is made up of around 7,000,000,000,000,000,000,000,000,000,000 (7 octillion) atoms. Even more staggering is the fact that each individual atom is billions of years old.

Turn back time tips

Ease a chesty cough by making a quick vapour rub using a teaspoon of olive oil and few drops of eucalyptus essential oil. Rub it on for immediate relief.

Great days out

Bolsover Castle

Bolsover, Derbyshire
We can't wait to see Bolsover's recently-restored Little Castle; a Jacobean treasure in which visitors are encouraged to sit on furniture and experience life as the owners would. Then, blow away the cobwebs on the Wall Walk, with views that stretch for miles. Reopened to the public for the first time in almost 400 years, you'll come away with a real sense of what castle life was like in the 1630s.
**Call 01246 822844 or visit
www.english-heritage.org/bolsovercastle**

It made me laugh

My husband has a saying that always makes me laugh: "When a woman is dressed to kill, it's generally her feet that are the first victims." Most men will have suffered their wives complaining about her high heels enough to understand just what he means!
J Williams, Liverpool, Merseyside

Recipe of the week

Tomato and Lentil Soup

Serves: 6
Preparation time: 10 minutes
Cooking time: 40 minutes

200g (7oz) split red lentils, rinsed
2ltr (3¹/₂pt) stock
450g (14oz) frozen diced vegetable mix (onion, carrot and celery)
400g (13oz) chopped tomatoes
1 tbsp tomato purée
Parsley, basil or coriander to garnish

1 Place the lentils in a large saucepan. Pour in the stock and bring to the boil. Rapidly boil for 10 minutes then skim any froth from the surface.
2 Add the remaining ingredients, except garnish, and return to the boil.
3 Reduce the heat, cover and simmer for 30 minutes or until the lentils and vegetables are tender. Blend until smooth.
4 Serve with a sprinkling of herb garnish.
© www.coolcookery.co.uk

2   Monday

3   Tuesday

4   Wednesday

5   Thursday

6   Friday

7   Saturday

8   Sunday

Seems like only yesterday

The sun always shone

I was adopted at the age of six weeks and brought up in Sidmouth. I had a very happy childhood when it seemed the sun was always shining. Our house was only two miles from the sea and the children who lived in Fortescue Road – there were only seven of us – all used to play in an area of riverside meadows called The Byes. One of our games was to damn the stream with stones and then walk across it to the orchard on the other side.

This photo was taken of me in our large garden when I was about ten years old. I loved my long plaits; my hair was very dark and I had my plaits tied with red ribbons. Our dog, Kim, used to jump up and pull the ribbons off. When I was thirteen I had my hair cut really short and I hated it! I grew it long again, but it was never quite as long after that. My mum kept my cut-off plaits for ages.

The doll I am holding was called Mary. I wish I still had her, but when I grew up my parents gave her to another little girl who lived in our road who was also adopted. When I was 43 I traced my birth mother and, by coincidence, her name was also Mary.

Mrs Hazel Clapp, Sidmouth, Devon

It's a fact

The sandwich is one of the nation's favourite meals – and nowhere more so than in Yorkshire, where people spend an average of £114 each on the pre-packed treats – more than anywhere else in the UK. Meanwhile, folk in the South West spend the least, with an average of £55 a year.

Turn back time tips

Never skip mascara, particularly as you get older when your features need a helping hand to stand out. Switch to brown mascara, which is softer than black and for a fuller flutter lightly dust a translucent powder over your lashes before applying a volume boosting mascara. This gives the mascara something to hold on to and helps lashes look thicker.

Great days out

Jackfield Tile Museum

Nr. Ironbridge, Shropshire
For spectacular period rooms filled with gorgeous tiles, look no further than this little gem. The factory complex is part of the Ironbridge Gorge Museums, and it houses five differently-themed galleries. Explore a replica of Covent Garden underground station before deciphering the nursery rhymes from the tiles of a children's hospital ward and reliving those front rooms typical of the Thirties. **Call 01952 433424 or visit www.ironbridge.org.uk**

It made me laugh

A man went into hospital to have an ear transplant, but was given a pig's ear instead of a human one. When he went back for a check-up, the Doctor asked him how his hearing was. "It's fine," said the man, "but I do get a lot of crackling." **Mrs D Clarke, Bristol**

Recipe of the week

Apricot and Almond Slice

Makes: 8 slices
Preparation time: 10 minutes
Cooking time: 35 minutes

100g (3½oz) rolled oats
150g (5oz) flaked almonds
2 tsp baking powder
100g (3½oz) golden caster sugar, plus 2 tsp to sprinkle
2 medium eggs, beaten
2 pieces stem ginger from a jar, chopped
150g (5oz) soft dried apricots, roughly chopped

1 Preheat the oven to 180°C/350°F/Gas Mark 4. Grease a 450g (14oz) loaf tin and line the base and sides with greased greaseproof paper.
2 Blend 50g (2oz) oats until finely ground. Tip into a bowl. Blend half the flaked almonds until ground and add to the bowl with the rolled oats, baking powder, caster sugar and all but 2 tbsp of the remaining flaked almonds.
3 Mix the eggs with the ginger and 75ml (3floz) cold water. Add to the bowl, along with the chopped apricots. Mix well, then turn into the tin and scatter with the reserved almonds.
4 Bake for 30–35 minutes until golden and just firm. Loosen the cake at the ends then lift out onto a wire rack. Sprinkle with remaining sugar and leave to cool. Serve thinly sliced.

Top tip: 1 tsp ground ginger or mixed spice can be used instead of stem ginger
© www.allaboutoats.com

9 Monday

10 Tuesday

11 Wednesday

12 Thursday

13 Friday

14 Saturday

15 Sunday

Seems like only yesterday

The truth will out!

During the war my infant school teacher, Mrs Morse, kept a diary in which she recorded events told to her by her pupils. Nearly every child had something to contribute to the diary, but as I didn't have anything to record I decided, one morning, that I would make up a story. And what a story it was!

At the time my father, Reg, was serving as a gunner in the Royal Navy. I told the class that he had died. The news soon spread around our small town of Watchet where, in those days, everyone knew everyone. Naturally, they all felt very sad for my little brother Gowen and me. The first my mother knew of it was when friends told her they were very sorry to hear that Reg had died.

I can still remember the telling-off I had. That page of Mrs Morse's diary was torn out and I was never allowed to put anything in it again. It certainly taught me to be truthful at all times.

The photograph of my mother, Gowen and me was taken to send to my father when he was many miles from home. And thankfully he did return safely to us at the end of the war.

Mrs Jenny Hill, Watchet, Somerset

It made me laugh

I had to laugh recently when I looked in the window of our local carpet shop. The owner had put a notice in the window: "I haven't got 50 Shades of Grey but I've got 100 shades of beige!"

Sheila Bennett, Daventry, Northamptonshire

It's a fact

Six years ago, a retired policeman called Geraint Woolford was admitted to Abergale Hospital in North Wales and was left next to another retired policeman called Geraint Woolford. The men had never met, weren't related and were the only two people in the UK called Geraint Woolford.

Turn back time tips

Experts reckon that sleeping on your side can cause sleep lines that, over time, become permanent wrinkles. Luckily swapping your cotton pillowcase for silk could be the simple solution. Unlike cotton, silk slides against the skin rather than creating friction benefitting both skin and hair. Silk also absorbs less moisture so you'll wake up to skin that's more hydrated.

Great days out

PIC: HAREWOOD HOUSE TRUST

Harewood House

Leeds, West Yorkshire
The spectacular grounds at Harewood are worth shouting about – as the Tour de France cyclists should know, as they sped through here last July! For those of us who prefer a calm amble, the Bird Garden is renowned for its penguins (yes, penguins) and there's plenty of art and history to discover, too. Winter's openings are for a series of Members-only Tours and Talks, which are worth it if you want the insider info. **Call 01132 181010 or visit www.harewood.org**

Recipe of the week

Heart's Desire Cake

Makes: 1 loaf cake
Preparation time: 20 minutes, plus 30 minutes freezing, 10 cooling and 30 chilling
Cooking time: 2 hours

Heart cake
125g (4$^{1}/_{2}$oz) baking margarine
125g (4$^{1}/_{2}$oz) caster sugar
2 medium eggs
200g (7oz) plain flour
2 tsp baking powder
Red food colouring
Chocolate cake
115g (4oz) baking margarine
115g (4oz) caster sugar
2 medium eggs, beaten
1 tsp vanilla extract
100g (3$^{1}/_{2}$oz) plain flour
25g (1oz) cocoa powder
1 tsp baking powder
To decorate
75g (3oz) dark chocolate
40g (1$^{1}/_{2}$ oz) unsalted butter

1 Preheat oven to 180°C/350°F/Gas Mark 4. Lightly grease a 450g (1lb) loaf tin. Mix heart cake ingredients together, add food colouring, and spoon into the tin. Bake for 1 hour until risen and firm. Turn out on to a rack after 5 minutes, to cool.
2 Discard the ends, then cut into 7 slices. Cut a heart shape from each slice then freeze all for 30 minutes.
3 Wash the tin and re-grease. Mix chocolate cake ingredients, then thickly spread over the bottom and sides of the tin. Arrange the sponge hearts upright in the tin; close enough to support each other. Carefully spoon over the remaining mixture.
4 Bake for 50 minutes until risen and firm. Turn out after 10 minutes, to cool on a wire rack.
5 Melt the dark chocolate and butter together then cool for 20 minutes, before topping the cake. Chill for 30 minutes only before serving.
© www.facebook.com/DrOetkerBaking

16 Monday

17 Tuesday

18 Wednesday

19 Thursday

20 Friday

21 Saturday

22 Sunday

Seems like only yesterday

War and peace

My earliest recollection is of sitting in a high chair, banging a saucepan lid. My father was a grocer and we lived above the shop. When I was about 18 months old he cut his hand badly. I was upset by this and to comfort me my mother gave me a pink rabbit made by the well-known toy maker, Merrythought. The rabbit was christened Der-der and I have it to this day.

When war broke out, Dad joined the Auxiliary Fire Service in Ashford in Middlesex. One terrible night, he didn't come home because he was in London, fighting the Blitz. When he arrived back he was red-eyed with fatigue and slept for eight hours before returning to the scene.

The air raids worsened and in 1944 my mother and I moved away to Eastington Rectory near Stroud. We returned the following year but had to live with my grandmother until we could move back into our own home which had been occupied by victims of the bombing.

After the war ended, things returned to normal – I was able to walk to school and play happily outside with neighbouring children. In some ways, life was still austere as food was rationed and we had to queue to buy it. In 1948 I progressed to the local grammar school where I soon made friends and especially enjoyed history lessons. I kept in contact with my history teacher after I had left to become a teacher myself.

Mrs Jean Odell, Hampton, Middx

It's a fact

The world's biggest pancake was cooked in Rochdale in 1994. It measured 15m in diameter, weighed three tonnes and contained a colossal 2 million calories. The record for the biggest number of pancake tosses in Britain was 349 in two minutes.

Turn back time tips

Have an avocado with your lunch and you're less likely to snack in the afternoon and may well eat less at dinner too. Avocados help to keep you feeling fuller for longer.

Great days out

Llyn Peninsula

Cwrt, Gwynedd

The 30 miles of Llyn peninsula, Gateway to the Sound, lies at the edge of Wales. Its dramatic and beautiful setting is now also home to a Coastal Tourism Centre, which means there's a perfect wet-weather activity just waiting for you. Learn about local history before heading out to hear almost three-quarters of today's inhabitants speaking in Welsh! Then there's the lost mining village of Nant Gwrtheyrn – which hosts Welsh language courses. **Call 01758 760469 or visit www.nationaltrust.org.uk/llyn-peninsula**

It made me laugh

A boy was in school and the teacher asked him if he'd done his homework. He said he hadn't, and the teacher then said to him that he would be put in detention. "That's not fair," said the boy. "How can you punish me for something I haven't done?"

Mr R Twinley, Dereham, Norfolk

Recipe of the week

Herby Pork Meatballs with Cranberry Gravy

Serves: 6
Preparation time: 15 minutes
Cooking time: 20 minutes

250g (8oz) minced pork
250g (8oz) sausagemeat
2 tsp fresh sage, finely chopped
2 garlic cloves, peeled and crushed
5 tbsp cranberry sauce
Salt and pepper
2 tbsp olive oil
2 shallots, peeled and finely chopped
1 yellow pepper, deseeded and chopped
450ml ($^3/_4$pt) beef stock
1 tbsp cornflour
2 tbsp tomato purée

1 Mix together the pork, sausagement, sage, garlic and 1 tbsp cranberry sauce. Season to taste and stir through.
2 With damp hands, shape into 24 small, even-sized balls. Heat the olive oil in a deep frying pan and fry the meatballs in batches until brown all over. Drain from the pan with a slotted spoon and set aside.
3 Drain all but 1 tbsp fat from the pan, add the shallots and pepper and fry gently until softened. Stir in the remaining cranberry sauce and keep stirring.
4 Mix a little stock with the cornflour until smooth and add to the pan with the remaining stock and tomato purée. Stir constantly until the sauce is thickened and smooth. Return the meatballs to the pan.
5 Cover and cook over low heat for 15 minutes, occasionally basting the meatballs with the sauce. Serve with pasta.
© www.oceanspray.co.uk

February 23 - March 1

23 Monday

24 Tuesday

25 Wednesday

26 Thursday

27 Friday

28 Saturday

1 Sunday

Seems like only yesterday

My life in handbags

This photo, taken at a wedding in 1960, shows how a well-turned-out four year old accessorised her outfit! I remember this little bag well. It had a gold clasp and probably contained my embroidered hanky, some sweets and a few sixpences in my Cinderella purse.

By the age of seven I had moved on to a Beatle bag, a square tartan creation with a black fringe and a long patent leather strap. I took it to school and kept my crisps for lunchtime in it along with my 'teenage' doll. For my holiday I had an on-trend bag with lots of pockets in it.

As a teenager in the Seventies I used to save up my pocket money and go to the local market to buy my bags. One year I bought a red plastic shoulder bag for £1.50. My sixteenth birthday saw me searching out a black patent bag with a bright yellow stripe to match my platform shoes. In 1974 I invested in a sophisticated cream box bag that matched my outsize cream beads, earrings and beige wedge sandals.

Although I have never had the designer bags carried by the stars of stage and screen, I think mine have given me just as much pleasure from an early age. My friends often tease me that I am never seen without a handbag.

Linda Sherlock, Chorley, Lancs

It made me laugh

I always chuckle at this note that was once left for a milkman: 'My daughter says she wants a milkshake. Do you do it before you deliver, or do I have to shake the bottle afterwards?'

Barbara Carter, Abingdon, Oxfordshire

It's a fact

The phrase 'lightning never strikes twice' turns out not to be true. Although it is quite rare, lightning can strike the same place more than once. There are about 16 million lightning storms around the world every year, with about 100 lightning flashes happening every second. There are numerous different types of lightning, many of which have rather evocative names including sprites, blue jets and elves.

Turn back time tips

Don't be afraid to try out the latest fashion trends, just remember these golden rules. Consider whether the shape will suit you and if it will work with your existing wardrobe. Stick to wearing one style trend at a time and team with more classic items. If you're unsure go for trend-inspired accessories.

Great days out

Victorian Games at Audley End House and Gardens

Saffron Walden, Essex, Feb 23-27
It's games galore at Audley End this half term... Skittles, quoits, and even chess will have your youngsters playing like a pro and using their heads! For a family day out away from the telly, it's just £1 extra to take part, on top of your entrance fee to house and g rounds. Audley's not usually open at this time of year, so don't miss out. 10am-6pm.
Call 0870 333 1181 or visit
www.english-heritage.org.uk/audley

Recipe of the week

Lamb Wellington

Serves: 4
Preparation time: 25 minutes
Cooking time: 25 minutes

2 lamb neck fillets, approx. 230g (7½oz) each
Seasoning
2 sprigs rosemary, finely chopped
3 tbsp olive oil
150g (5oz) chestnut mushrooms, finely chopped
2 leeks, finely chopped
2 cloves garlic, crushed
100ml (3½floz) white wine
500g packet pre-made puff pastry
1 egg, beaten

1 Preheat the oven to 200°C/400°F/Gas Mark 6.
2 Season the lamb and roll in rosemary. Heat half the oil in a frying pan and sear the lamb on all sides until brown all over. Remove and set aside.
3 Heat the remaining oil in the pan and gently fry the mushrooms, leeks and garlic for 3-4 minutes. Stir in the wine and cook until evaporated. Cool slightly.
4 Cut the pastry block in half and roll into a large rectangle 5mm thick, big enough to wrap around the lamb. Spoon half the mushroom mixture along the centre and place the lamb on top. Brush exposed pastry with beaten egg, then wrap around the meat. Trim any excess.
5 Repeat for the second piece of lamb, then place both on a baking tray, seams down. Brush with remaining egg.
6 Bake for 20-25 minutes until golden brown, then leave to rest for 10 minutes before serving.
© www.eatwelshlamb.co.uk

March 2 - 8

2 Monday

3 Tuesday

4 Wednesday

5 Thursday

6 Friday

7 Saturday

8 Sunday

Seems like only yesterday

Christina (left) wanted to look her best for her confirmation

My first must-have shoes

Whenever I see a pair of tan shoes in a shop window it reminds me of when I was about ten years old, living in Ireland and about to make my first confirmation. As it was wintertime, we were to wear hats and coats instead of dresses and veils.

I had almost all of my outfit except for the shoes so Mum took me to town to buy them. We had strict instructions from Dad to get sensible shoes. After looking in several shops I spotted a beautiful pair of tan shoes. It took a lot of begging and pleading for Mum to give in because sensible shoes they were not.

All the way home we rehearsed what to tell Dad. To our great surprise, he didn't hit the roof but just smiled at me going on and on about how they would match my tan hat, tan gloves and green coat.

At last the great day arrived. I jumped out of bed to find, horror of horrors, it had snowed during the night and there were about three inches covering the ground. There was no way I could wear my lovely shoes. I cried all the way to the church. Well, wouldn't you have done if you'd had to cover all your finery with a raincoat and wear your old wellies?

Mrs Christina Kelly, Worcester

It made me laugh

When I go to someone's house and they say, "Make yourself at home", the first thing I do is throw them out because I don't like visitors!

Jennifer Shelden, Leicester

It's a fact

If you think the NHS needs improvement, just be glad you weren't alive in the Middle Ages, when people believed that sitting in a sewer, shaving a live chicken's bottom and strapping it to your armpit would cure the Black Death. But that's nothing on Ancient Egyptian medicine, which prescribed pouring liquefied pigs eyes into a patient's ear to treat blindness.

Turn back time tips

Stand on one leg for as long as you can everyday. Keep a chair near by in case you wobble. Repeat on the other side. It should help to improve your balance which, in turn, could help to reduce your risk of a fall.

Great days out

The Sugarcraft, Cake Decorating and Baking Show

Event City Halls, Manchester, Mar 6-8
Budding sugarcrafters, skilled bakers and cake-lovers unite! It's Cake International this weekend. Marvel at towering cake perfection and unbelievably intricate detail before picking up your own baking supplies. Take part in workshops, learn from the various demonstrations, or visit the authors' area and kitchen for a chance to spy some famous faces. **Call 01425 272711 for general enquiries and 01425 277988 for tickets. Visit www.cakeinternational.co.uk**

Recipe of the week

Apple Meringue Pie

Serves: 6-8
Preparation time: 30 minutes
Cooking time: 40 minutes

225g (7$\frac{1}{2}$oz) plain flour
115g (4oz) unsalted butter, cubed
Pinch salt
1 medium egg
2 tbsp cold water
1kg (2lb) cooking apples
Juice and zest of 2 lemons
2 tbsp cold water
4 medium eggs (separated into yolks and whites)
205g (7$\frac{1}{4}$oz) caster sugar
25g (1oz) salted butter, cubed
Pinch cream of tartar
80g (3$\frac{1}{4}$oz) sieved icing sugar
2 tsp mixed spice
2 tsp granulated sugar

1 Preheat oven to 200°C/400°F/Gas Mark 6. Rub together butter, flour and salt, add 1 egg and water to make pastry.
2 Roll out, then transfer to a 25cm (11in) flan ring. Prick and line with greaseproof paper. Cook 'blind' with baking beans for 20 minutes.
3 Cut apples into small pieces. Cook into pulp, over low heat with lemon juice, zest and water. Cool for 10 minutes. Stir in egg yolks, butter and 125g caster sugar.
4 Pour into base and cook until just set (about 25 minutes). Remove from oven before setting temperature at 230°C/450°F/Gas Mark 8.
5 Whisk egg whites and cream of tartar until foamy, then introduce the remaining caster sugar. Finally add icing sugar and spice. Top flan with meringue, sprinkle with sugar, and brown in oven before serving.
© www.bramleyapples.co.uk

9 Monday

10 Tuesday

11 Wednesday

12 Thursday

13 Friday

14 Saturday

15 Sunday

Seems like only yesterday

Left to right, **Peggy, Terry, George, Patricia and Joan**

Homesick for Hampshire

In our family we call this the Bisto Kids picture. It was taken in 1946 when my brothers and sisters and I had moved back to Mile End in East London after being evacuated. I am the boy in the middle; I may be smiling, but I was sorry to leave the country life we had enjoyed in the small village of Shipton Bellinger in Hampshire.

Luckily, our dad had survived the war and when he was demobbed he decided that we should all move back to Mile End where he and my mother still had family. In the photo I am back to being a Cockney, but I was not happy.

I still have vivid memories of Shipton Bellinger, the farm, the school, the shop and the village pub, as well as the freedom of rivers and hills and countryside that stretched to the horizon. For a while, we lived opposite a large American camp that seemed to spring up almost overnight. The main gates were across the road from our school and we got on well with the soldiers who often gave us chewing gum.

There are only five of us in the photo, but we numbered 12 in all. The Whites were the largest family in Eric Street. For a short time we lived at number 74, next-door to the Bresslaw family. (Bernard Bresslaw was later to become a star in the Carry On films.)

George F White, Peterborough, Cambs

It made me laugh

It was almost Mothers' Day, and my friend knelt down in the grass to pick some daffodils to give to her mum. After picking half a dozen or so she got up, and I saw that she had knelt in dog poo! Her black wool stockings were a mess! We were just nine years old then, but it still makes me laugh to this day.

Marion Ward, Colchester, Essex

It's a fact

Up until 1908, the Olympic marathon race was always an approximate distance. In that particular year, the Royal family requested that the marathon start inside the grounds of Windsor Castle so that their children could witness its start. The distance from Windsor Castle to the Olympic Stadium was 42,195 metres (or 26 miles and 385 yards), and this length remains in place for races today.

Turn back time tips

Have a low-fat yogurt before you exercise; it's a good source of protein which could help to boost your metabolism so you'll burn more calories while you workout. Protein also helps to build muscle, keeping you strong.

Great days out

Lambing courses

Hare Farm Hideaway, Rye, Sussex
It wouldn't be spring without lambs! This month Hare Farm will offer evening and day courses to give us all a taste of life as a Victorian shepherd. No matter whether you're a town or country mouse, you'll cover birthing, feeding and marking. You can even splash out on a night in a replica shepherd's hut, with all mod cons inside. Various dates available (and subject to change), but spaces are limited – **call 07802 979348 or visit www.harefarmhideaways.co.uk**

Recipe of the week

Massaman Curry

Serves: 4
Preparation time: 20 minutes
Cooking time: 25 minutes

1 tbsp rapeseed or olive oil
1 onion, peeled and sliced
2 tbsp Massaman curry paste
450g (1lb) lean beef or lamb strips
400ml (14floz) can coconut milk
2 tbsp crunchy peanut butter
150ml ($^1/_4$pt) good quality hot beef or lamb stock
1 tbsp fish sauce
450g (1lb) small new potatoes, unpeeled and cut into quarters
Salt and freshly-ground black pepper
25g (1oz) roughly chopped roasted unsalted peanuts, to garnish
Large handful of freshly chopped coriander, to garnish (optional)

1 Heat the oil in a large non-stick pan, add the onion and cook for 2-3 minutes.
2 Stir in the curry paste and cook for 1-2 minutes. Add the beef or lamb strips and cook for 2-3 minutes.
3 Add the coconut milk, peanut butter, stock and fish sauce. Bring to the boil. Add the potatoes, reduce the heat, cover and simmer for 15-20 minutes, or until the potatoes are cooked. Season to taste.
4 Garnish with unsalted roasted peanuts and freshly chopped coriander (if used). Serve with boiled rice and seasonal vegetables.
© www.simplybeefandlamb.co.uk

March 16 - 22

16 Monday

17 Tuesday

18 Wednesday

19 Thursday

20 Friday

21 Saturday

22 Sunday

Seems like only yesterday

Back-to-back living

For the first 16 years of my life I lived with my parents and younger brother in a back-to-back terraced house. The houses all had different coloured doorsteps; ours was yellow from being scoured with yellowstone, next-door's was the colour of Cardinal red polish and two houses further down the street had natural stone with white edges.

We had a cellar with a couple of shelves over the stairs and behind the door was a billhook on which were hung paid bills. There was an old gas mantle still on the wall of Mum and Dad's bedroom although they had paid £25 to have electricity put in.

A tin bath was hung on a wall and brought into the main room where it was placed on the rug in front of the Yorkist cast-iron fire range (later replaced with a 'modern' tiled fireplace). We each waited in the bedroom until it was our turn to have a bath. Afterwards, we used saucepans to empty the bath. Our toilet was in a block two minutes away down the road.

I slept in the big attic bedroom. I wanted it to be pink so Dad mixed cochineal with cream paint to get the right colour. When I was a teenager, the walls were covered with posters of Billy Fury and Cliff Richard taken from the centre pages of the Valentine magazine.

Patricia Mason, Skipton, N Yorks

It's a fact

There is no 'dark side of the moon', because in reality both sides receive the same amount of sunlight. However, only one side is ever actually seen from Earth, because the moon rotates on its axis in exactly the same time as it takes to orbit us. The far side has only been seen by the human eye from a spacecraft.

Turn back time tips

Cut down on alcohol and salt for younger looking skin. Too much salt encourages fluid retention, which can make skin look puffy, while too much alcohol causes dehydration. Combined, both can make skin look dull and dry and can cause puffiness in delicate areas like under the eyes. Dehydrated skin will also make your wrinkles look far worse than they are.

Great days out

Total Solar Eclipse

Faroe Islands, off Scotland, Mar 20
Now, this is a once-in-a-lifetime opportunity that will take place at precisely 9.41am – and the unspoilt Faroe Islands will be one of only two places in the world from where this total solar eclipse will be seen. They're home to just 40,000 people and a whopping 70,000 sheep! A special direct flight will be operated from London by Atlantic Airways. **For more information visit www.solareclipse.fo or email booking@atlantic.fo**

It made me laugh

Q: What's the most common owl in the UK?
A: A tea towel.

Judi James, Pembrokeshire

Recipe of the week

Lemon Poppy Seed Muffins

Makes: 12
Preparation time: 15 minutes
Cooking time: 20 minutes

Zest of 2 lemons
98g (3¹/₂oz) Truvia® Baking Blend
260g (8¹/₂oz) plain flour
2 tsp baking powder
¹/₄ tsp bicarbonate of soda
¹/₄ tsp salt
190g (6³/₄oz) reduced-fat sour cream
2 eggs
1¹/₂ tsp vanilla extract
110g (4oz) unsalted butter, softened
Juice of 1 lemon
2 tbsp poppy seeds
Glaze:
98g (3¹/₂oz) Truvia® Baking Blend, ground in a coffee grinder
Juice of 1 lemon

1 Preheat oven to 200°C/400°F/Gas Mark 6.
2 In a large bowl, combine the lemon zest, Truvia® Baking Blend, flour, baking powder, bicarbonate of soda and salt.
3 In a smaller bowl, combine sour cream, eggs, vanilla, butter and lemon juice and whisk together until smooth.
4 Add the sour cream mixture to the flour mixture. Gently combine, then fold in the poppy seeds.
5 Divide batter evenly into paper-lined muffin cups, and bake for 18 minutes, or until a toothpick comes out clean.
7 Prepare glaze by mixing lemon juice with ground Truvia® Baking Blend, then brush or drizzle over cooked muffins.
© www.truvia.co.uk

23 Monday

24 Tuesday

25 Wednesday

26 Thursday

27 Friday

28 Saturday

29 Sunday

Seems like only yesterday

Rites of passage

When I was growing up the term 'yummy mummy' had not yet been invented. My mum could never have been mistaken for my sister and the lines differentiating parents and children were never blurred. We still had rites of passage, so I didn't have my first bike until the age of ten and I only had my first wristwatch when I could tell the time.

When I was 13 I started going to the youth club in our village when I was allowed to wear stockings for the first time. This was in 1961 and tights had not yet come into being. The fashionable items of that era were a big 'sloppy Joe' jumper, a silk Paisley blouse and mohair pencil skirt. In the summer we wore dresses with full skirts with layers of frothy net petticoats underneath.

I had seen one of these net creations in the Co-op shop window when we girls sneaked out of school in the lunch hour. After months of nagging my mum for one of these petticoats, one duly appeared on Christmas morning. With my newly acquired first pair of high-heeled shoes, I had all the gear. Now all I needed was the boyfriend, but that's another story...

Mrs P Bayley, Southampton

It's a fact

It's estimated that up to 7,000 different languages are spoken around the world, 90 per cent of which are used by fewer than 100,000 people. Asia has the largest variety of spoken languages, at 2,200, while Europe has a mere 260. Amazingly, there are 46 languages which remain worldwide with just one single speaker!

Turn back time tips

A good outfit starts with good foundations and a sagging bust will instantly age you, so go and get properly measured and invest in a good supportive bra. For special occasions consider shapewear that will smooth lumps and bumps for a streamlined silhouette.

Great days out

Miniatura: Life in Miniature exhibition

NEC, Birmingham
That ideal home might just be in reach, at this larger-than-life exhibition of the tiny and intricate. Dolls' houses come in all styles, from medieval to post-war, with interiors to match – and it's here that keen 'miniaturists' gather to ooh and ahh at the latest creations. Perhaps, downsizing really is inevitable... The spring exhibition usually takes place at the end of March. **For more information call the ticket hotline on 0121 767 4100 or visit www.miniatura.co.uk**

It made me laugh

My grandson and I were discussing our cat Chelsy's upcoming second birthday, and we were planning to give her a 'party'. Later, I was telling his mum all about our plans, when my grandson suddenly said urgently: "Ssh Nan! You'll spoil the surprise – Chelsy is listening!" **S. Stoner, Plymouth, Devon**

Recipe of the week

Miso Soup

Serves: 2
Preparation time: 15 minutes
Cooking time: 10 minutes

110g (3³/₄oz) Japanese soba noodles (100% buckwheat)
1l (1³/₄pt) chicken stock
50g (2oz) miso paste
120g (4oz) boneless, skinless, dark chicken meat cut into strips or Tofu
1 egg, beaten
1 tbsp cornflower
2 garlic cloves, minced
1 small carrot, grated
¹/₂ leek, finely sliced
Handful beansprouts
12 pieces canned bamboo shoots
2 tbsp peanut oil
2 tbsp low-salt soya sauce
2 tsp sugar
Chilli oil, to taste
1 tsp toasted sesame seeds

1 Boil the noodles for 2-3 minutes then drain. Bring the stock to boil.
2 Press the miso through a sieve so it's extra smooth, then whisk into the stock. Cover and remove from heat. Combine the egg and cornflour, season, then add the chicken pieces to coat.
3 Heat the oil in a wok over a medium heat. Throw in the garlic for a few seconds then add the chicken, carrot, leek and beansprouts. Stir-fry for 4 minutes. Add the soya sauce and sugar and cook for another minute.
4 Divide noodles between 2 bowls and ladle over the stock, topping with vegetable mix, chilli oil and sesame seeds.
© www.livlifefoods.co.uk

30 Monday

31 Tuesday

1 Wednesday

2 Thursday

3 Friday

4 Saturday

5 Sunday

Seems like only yesterday

Guiding for girls

Growing up as an only child on a new estate was quite lonely until my friend Valerie introduced me to the Girls' Life Brigade at the Methodist church. This was marvellous because we learned all kinds of interesting things as well as taking parts in social events like fancy dress parties. I even loved Sunday School because we could collect pretty little Bible texts – not that I understood them!

Soon after this, my friend Jean Mac came up to me full of excitement and said: "Why don't you come to Guides with me? They go camping and tracking and go in for all kinds of badges!" So, yes, I abandoned Valerie and joined the Girl Guides! What kind of friend was I? But moneywise, it had to be either one or the other and the more 'Boy Scout' type of activities of the Guides really appealed to me.

I joined the 3rd Hillingdon Girl Guides and we went camping and had campfires. I became a patrol leader, then a company leader, and stayed with the Guides until I was 16. I didn't take up the offer of going on to the next stage, the Sea Rangers as they were called then. I'd started work and suddenly felt I was too grown up for all that.

Barbara Bignell, Kettering, Northants

It's a fact

The English language is a peculiar thing – we pronounce 'ough' in nine different ways. This sentence contains all of them: A rough-coated, dough-faced, thoughtful ploughman strode through Scarborough; after falling into a slough, he coughed and hiccoughed!

Turn back time tips

While it's great to find a cut that suits your face shape, don't be afraid to try something new with an occasional update. A subtle change of colour or a few more layers will make a difference. If forehead wrinkles are a bugbear try a fringe – it's youthful and great for hiding frown lines!

Great days out

Chester Food and Drink Festival

Chester Racecourse, Apr 4-6
For something a bit different this Easter, head over to Chester and get your taste buds tingling. Whether you fancy a weekend away, or just a simple day of family fun, make the most of the many exhibitions, demonstrations and good, clean, (hygienic!) fun. With a celebrity appearance or two, and plenty of chances to taste the best of the area, what's not to love? **Call 01244 405615 or visit www.chesterfoodanddrink.co.uk**

It made me laugh

Police arrested two people – one for stealing batteries and the other for stealing fireworks. They charged one and let the other off.
Richard Brooks, Barnsley, South Yorkshire

Recipe of the week

Cranberry and Orange Roast Salmon

Serves: 6
Preparation time: 20 minutes
Cooking time: 1 hour 5 minutes

2 x 550g (1lb4oz) skinned, salmon fillets
Salt and pepper
Large knob of butter
1 small onion, finely diced
50g (2oz) basmati rice
50g (2oz) fresh white breadcrumbs
1 tbsp fresh chopped dill
1 egg yolk
85g (3^1/$_4$oz) dried cranberries
2 oranges
4 tbsp cranberry sauce

1 Preheat oven to 200°C/400°F/Gas mark 6. Season fillets and put one on an oiled baking sheet.
2 Melt butter in a pan and fry the onion for 3–4 minutes. Sprinkle over rice and season with salt. Pour in 100ml (3^1/$_2$floz) cold water and bring to the boil, then cover and turn to lowest heat for 10 minutes (do not lift the lid).
3 Tip into a bowl and stir in the breadcrumbs, dill, egg yolk and cranberries.
4 Cut 3 thin orange slices, then juice and zest both oranges. Mix the zest into the stuffing, season to taste, and spoon over the salmon on the baking sheet. Place the remaining salmon fillet over the stuffing. Top with reserved orange slices and tie at intervals.
5 Mix the orange juice and cranberry sauce and spoon over. Cover with foil and roast for 25 minutes. Remove foil and roast for another 25 minutes.
© www.oceanspray.co.uk

6 Monday

7 Tuesday

8 Wednesday

9 Thursday

10 Friday

11 Saturday

12 Sunday

Seems like only yesterday

Dapper mum and dad

I was brought up listening to Elvis Presley, Bill Haley and the Comets and Frank Sinatra. These were the favourite singers of my mum and dad (Val and Pete) who were a typical couple of their day, always out dancing and dressed immaculately. Dad always took twice as long as Mum to get ready for a social occasion!

When I first saw this photo of them I thought they both looked extremely dapper in the 'Teddy Boy' fashion of that era. It was taken around 1957 when they were courting; Mum would have been 16 and Dad 19 years old. They had taken a day trip to the seaside and although it had started out dry it clouded over and began to rain heavily. They were caught unawares without an umbrella and were soaked through. Mum says her hair wasn't meant to look like that, all frizzy! To make matters worse, she was wearing plastic clip-on earrings in the shape of large daisies and the petals had dug into her cheek causing a bad skin reaction.

Sadly, Dad passed away two years ago, but Mum still loves to recall the memory of this day out together.

Debbie Whitten, Tunbridge Wells, Kent

It's a fact

After Queen Victoria and Christopher Columbus, Robert Burns has more statues dedicated to him around the world than any other non-religious figure. His famous New Year ditty Auld Lang Syne is recognised by the Guinness Book of World Records as being one of the top three most popular songs in the English language – the other two are Happy Birthday and For He's a Jolly Good Fellow.

Turn back time tips

Soothe a sore throat by mixing a tablespoon of honey in a cup of hot water with the juice of a lemon. Sip slowly to calm a scratchy throat.

Great days out

Traditional Market Town

Helmsley, North Yorkshire
For picture-postcard prettiness, you can't beat the only market town in the North York Moors National Park. Bookworms will love the independent bookshops, and even a seasoned shopper is sure to find something unusual in one of the many boutiques. Past the market square, there's the town castle to catch up on, as well as the Walled Gardens, and even the International Birds of Prey Centre at Duncome Park. **Visit www.visithelmsley.co.uk for more information.**

It made me laugh

Consider the poor hippopotamus:
His life is unduly monotonous.
He lives half asleep
At the edge of the deep,
And his face is as big as his bottom is.
Fiona Drummond, via email

Recipe of the week

Sunny Breakfast Skillet
Serves: 4
Preparation time: 5 minutes
Cooking time: 20 minutes

500g (1lb) diced potatoes
1 tbsp olive oil
5 rashers streaky bacon
5 pork chipolata sausages
8 cherry tomatoes, halved
Half a ciabatta loaf, cubed
4 large eggs, lightly beaten
100g (3 $^{1}/_{2}$ oz) natural Greek yogurt
Salt and pepper, to taste

1 Preheat the grill on high. Meanwhile, cook potatoes.
2 Heat a little olive oil in a frying pan. Add the bacon and sausages and stir often over high heat until cooked and brown. Now add the cooked potatoes, cherry tomatoes and ciabatta cubes.
3 Mix the eggs and yogurt, and season to taste. Pour into the pan and continue over high heat until sizzling and bubbling.
4 Transfer the pan to the grill and cook until golden brown and the egg has set. Serve with hot buttered toast.
© www.rachelsorganic.co.uk

13	Monday

14	Tuesday

15	Wednesday

16	Thursday

17	Friday

18	Saturday

19	Sunday

Seems like only yesterday

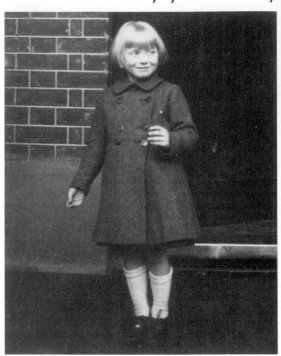

We knew how to party

I have fond memories of my 12th birthday party; it was a wartime party with just a few friends and a jelly-and-blancmange tea that my mother had somehow produced.

Parties then ended with home-grown entertainment. Someone sang, someone danced, and when it came to my turn I recited a poem about the wind. Each verse ended with a resounding 'Whoooo, whooo!' Soon everyone was joining in this chorus, only to be silenced by a knock on the door. It was the air-raid warden who scowled: "Hold your noise. People think it's an air-raid warning!" He hurried away amid giggles and cries of 'Rubbish!'

I remember another party that took place in a hall when I was an evacuee. As usual, it ended with audience participation. This time I recited an uncontroversial poem and was awarded a copy of Little Women. It was not quite my idea of a party as we all sat in rows being plied with bags of food, but I still treasure the book.

For my friend's birthday party we were promised a treat at teatime. What did we behold but banana sandwiches! No one had seen a real banana for years. The secret recipe (reluctantly revealed some time later) was parsnips mashed up with banana essence. My mother said: "Yuck!" But I have never tasted better bananas since.

Hooray for wartime parties and the gallant mothers who refused to let Hitler get them down!
Mrs Marion J Tobin, Whitbourne, Worcs

It's a fact

There is a species of snail called Ba humbugi. The Fijian mollusc is named after Scrooge's famous exclamation in A Christmas Carol, although Scrooge actually only utters the words 'Bah, humbug!' twice in the whole story (though he does exclaim 'Humbug!' a number of times).

Turn back time tips

Get an early night – scientists believe extra sleep allows your brain to carry out essential maintenance tasks, which could help to boost your memory.

Great days out

Rhug Estate

Corwen, Denbighshire
Lovers of farm and food should pay a visit to Lord Newborough's Organic Estate – it's one of the largest organic farms in the UK. His team proudly produces award-winning pies and pâtés aplenty (now, say that without your mouth full). Prince Charles and Camilla paid a visit way back in 2013, so we're eager to sample goods from the onsite shop and restaurant. **Call 01490 413000 or visit www.rhug.co.uk**

It made me laugh

Q: Why did the biscuit cry?
A: Because his mother had been a wafer so long.
Christine Gunn, Twycross, Warwickshire

Recipe of the week

Raspberry Oatmeal Bars
Makes: 24
Preparation time: 15 minutes
Cooking time: 40 minutes

200g (7oz) rolled oats
230g (7½oz) plain flour
1 tsp ground cinnamon
170g (5¾oz) unsalted butter, softened
½ tsp salt
1 tsp vanilla extract
65g (2½oz) Truvia® Baking Blend
Filling
440g (13¾oz) raspberries, fresh or frozen
65g (2½oz) Truvia® Baking Blend
2 tsp lemon juice
45g (1¾oz) cornflour

1 Preheat the oven to 160°C/325°F/Gas Mark 2 and grease and line a 33x23cm (13x9in) baking tin.
2 Place the oats, flour, cinnamon, butter, salt, vanilla and Truvia® Baking Blend into a bowl, and using a free-standing or hand-held mixer, mix on low speed for about 1 minute.
3 Scrape sides of bowl, then mix on medium speed for approx 2 minutes.
4 Pour two thirds into the prepared baking tin, and set aside the remaining third for topping. Press into the bottom to form a crust.
5 Make the filling by blending the raspberries, Truvia® Baking Blend, lemon juice and cornflour until evenly mixed. Spread over the oat mixture then top with the remaining oatmeal.
6 Bake for 35–40 minutes until golden brown, cut into squares while still warm, then leave to cool completely.
© www.truvia.co.uk

20 Monday

21 Tuesday

22 Wednesday

23 Thursday

24 Friday

25 Saturday

26 Sunday

Seems like only yesterday

My amazing dolls' house

In 1961 my father, a skilled carpenter, completed a gift for my 10th birthday that he had been working on for six years. After breakfast, he and Mum led me into the garden to see the surprise. I stared open-mouthed at the huge dolls' house, complete in every detail from the tiled roof to the hand-carved furniture and battery-operated lights. It was so fantastic that I didn't dare play with it, but contented myself with the many other generous gifts my parents gave me, their only child.

The following year my mother wrote to the Bethnal Green Museum offering the dolls' house as a gift to the nation. It was accepted and remained on exhibition there until the Eighties when it was put in store.

My father died in 1993, happy in the knowledge that his labour of love had been on display for decades. Since then I discovered, quite by chance, that the dolls' house was on display again, this time in the Architecture Gallery in the Victoria and Albert Museum.

On the centenary of his birth in February 2009 I visited the V & A to see the dolls' house (now described as 'a scale replica') I knew so well. As I took in the honour of my father's achievement being so fully recognised, I felt an emotion I still can't express. His creation is a permanent reminder of one man's intention of making a long-lasting gift for his daughter.

Mrs Katharine Easton, London SE4

It's a fact

Many tube stations were used as air-raid shelters during the Second World War, but the Central Line was even converted into a fighter aircraft factory that stretched for more than two miles, with its own railway system. Its existence remained an official secret until the Eighties.

Turn back time tips

If you, or your partner snore try singing – singing helps to strengthen your throat muscles which could help to reduce the amount you snore. Any song works, so sing along to your favourite track every day.

Great days out

PIC: MIKE KIPLING

Castle Howard

York, North Yorkshire

Impressively, Castle Howard is still home to the Howard family – but don't let that get in the way of a good nose around this 18th century beauty. The farm shop, garden centre and café are all what you'd expect from a top-notch establishment; plus the Atlas Fountain is one of several impressive water features you need to see. Recognise anything? Maybe you've glimpsed it in the BBC adaptation of Death Comes to Pemberley. **Call 01653 648444 or visit www.castlehoward.co.uk**

It made me laugh

I had learnt a great technique for remembering names, which was to associate the name with a picture of some kind in your mind. I visited my new doctor, Dr Warburton, and had no difficulty associating his name with bread. On returning home my daughter asked me the name of the doctor and I replied: "Dr Hovis!"
M Braidman, Broseley, Shropshire

Recipe of the week

King Prawn Stir Fry with Lemongrass and Chilli

Serves 2
Preparation time: 15 minutes
Cooking time: 12 minutes

Small piece ginger, peeled and grated
1 stalk lemongrass, finely chopped
4 lime leaves, thinly sliced
4 tbsp fish sauce
1-2 tbsp palm sugar or light muscavado sugar
1 tbsp vegetable oil
10 raw king prawns, shells off but with tails if possible
1 small onion, cut into thick slices
1-2 small red Thai birds–eye chilli, finely chopped
3 cloves garlic, finely chopped
4 spring onions, cut into thumb length pieces
250g (8oz) asparagus, halved lengthways then cut into 2in pieces
Steamed Thai rice, fresh coriander and/or Thai basil to serve

1 Mix the ginger, lemongrass, lime leaves, fish sauce and sugar and put aside.
2 Heat a wok on high and when it's really hot add the oil. Once shimmering, add the prawns and stir-fry for 1–2 minutes until pink. Remove with a slotted spoon.
3 Throw in the onion and stir-fry for 2 minutes. Add the chilli, garlic and spring onions then stir–fry for a further 4 minutes. Re-introduce the prawns plus the asparagus for a further minute.
4 Finally pour over the sauce (from step1), and cook for about 3 minutes until sticky. Serve topped with fresh herbs and Thai rice.
© www.british-asparagus.co.uk

27 Monday

28 Tuesday

29 Wednesday

30 Thursday

1 Friday

2 Saturday

3 Sunday

Seems like only yesterday

Never a dull moment for a young Marlene and family

Life was an adventure

The youngest of four children, I was born a year before the Second World War broke out. We were never frightened by what was going on because we were taught to treat life as an adventure. There was an Anderson shelter in the front room where we could sleep eight people. (On one occasion my brother got into bed with his boots on!)

We had no central heating. In 1947 when the snow was thick on the ground outside, the ice was thick on the window inside.

Monday was always washing day and somehow or other it always got dried and was ironed on Tuesday. Meals – breakfast, dinner, tea and supper – were little and often. On Sunday we had a roast with cold meat on Monday. On Tuesday we had vegetable stew and dumplings, Wednesday was sausage and mash while Thursday was egg and chips and on Friday we had fish.

When I was ten my father died, leaving my disabled mother with four children under the age of 16 to bring up on her own. That summer my Uncle Mike took me out on his milk round. I was allowed to put milk from the churns into people's jugs (I don't suppose it would be allowed now). Then I sat in the back of the van with the door open while he drove to the next place. My reward was cracked eggs to take home to Mum and maybe a sixpence for me.

Mrs Marlene Wheatley, Chelmsford, Essex

It's a fact

The British Library receives a copy of every publication produced in the UK and Ireland, from magazines and newspapers to novels and journals, and has been doing so since 1662. If you looked at five items in the archive each day, it would take you more than 80,000 years to see the whole collection.

Turn back time tips

For youthful peepers start by applying a primer and then sweep a neutral-toned eyeshadow over the whole lid. Avoid sparkly metallic shadows, which highlight creases and lines; stick to matt formulas instead. Apply a slightly darker shade into the socket line blending well. Add a touch of highlighter under each brow arch and to the inner corner of each eye.

Great days out

Weald of Kent Craft & Design Show

Penshurst Place and Gardens, Tonbridge, May 2-4
Find unusual handmade crafts for the home and garden against the stunning backdrop of Penshurst. This show has been going strong for more than 30 years, thanks to crafting enthusiasts from all over the UK, and their exclusive wares. For further information call 01892 870307. An additional discounted charge will grant you access to the House and Gardens, too. **Visit www. ichfevents.co.uk and www.penshurstplace.com**

It made me laugh

Q: Why did Cleopatra refuse to see a psychiatrist?
A: She was the Queen of Denial.
                    Yvonne Foxton, Chesterfield, Derbyshire

Recipe of the week

GLUTEN & DAIRY FREE!

Apple and Carrot Cake
Serves:
Preparation time: 20 minutes
Cooking time: 40 minutes

175g (6oz) honey
175ml (6floz) sunflower oil
3 eggs
2 small apples, diced into 1cm pieces
150g (5oz) grated carrot
30g (1oz) walnuts, finely chopped
50g (2oz) raisins
50g (2oz) dates, finely chopped
Zest of 1 orange
170g (6oz) gluten-free flour
1 tsp bicarbonate soda
1 tsp baking powder
1 tsp ground cinnamon
$1/2$ tsp grated nutmeg
10g ($1/2$oz) linseeds

1 Preheat the oven to 170°C/340°F/Gas Mark $3^1/_2$, and line an 18cm (8in) tin with baking paper.
2 Mix the honey, oil and eggs until fluffy. Place the apple pieces in a bowl, cover with clingfilm and cook in the microwave for 5 minutes on high. Then add the apple to the egg mixture along with the grated carrot.
3 Add the walnuts, raisins, dates and orange zest. Mix well. Now sieve in the flour, bicarbonate of soda, baking powder, ground cinnamon, grated nutmeg and lightly mix.
4 Pour into the prepared tin and sprinkle with linseeds. Bake for 40 minutes. Leave to cool for 10 minutes, then turn out

Top tip: This will keep for up to 3 days in an airtight container
© www.detoxkitchen.co.uk

4	Monday
5	Tuesday
6	Wednesday
7	Thursday
8	Friday
9	Saturday
10	Sunday

Seems like only yesterday

Happy holiday days with the Brownies

I was a pinball wizard

This photo is of me (on the left) with my friends Valerie and Pauline when we were aged about seven or eight. It was taken when we were on a Brownies' holiday at the Children's Inn at Rowarth in the Peak District. We travelled there by bus from Stockport. The Inn was quite an old building with panelled walls and wooden floors scattered with rag rugs. I was fascinated by the door at the bottom of the stairs that closed them off from the room.

While we were there we all made our own beds and shared the chores which included taking it in turns to pump the water outside in the yard. We also laid the tables and swept the floors.

During the day we went for walks around the area. After supper we had sing-songs or played ludo, snakes and ladders, cards and dominoes. I was enthralled by the bagatelle board (a pinball game) as I had never seen one before. I decided to ask for one for Christmas and was ecstatic when my wish was eventually granted.

I had two wonderful holidays at the Children's Inn. Sadly, I lost touch with Valerie and Pauline as we all went to different schools after we left primary school.

Mrs Jane Bonnick, Tiverton, Devon

It's a fact

If all of the UK's Girl Guides held hands in a straight line it would stretch an impressive 850km – longer than 8,095 buses parked end to end! They could also circle the M25 four and a half times and reach from Bristol to Inverness. Let's hope there's a badge for that.

Turn back time tips

Summer pastel shades are often big for spring and summer, but when worn together they can look a bit too girly. Instead team with neutrals – white and grey are great choices and look gorgeous teamed with mint green or pale blue. Otherwise, add pastel accessories to a simple crisp white outfit – an easy way to look on-trend without over doing it.

Great days out

Yeo Valley Organic Garden Plant Fair

Holt Farm, Blagdon, Somerset
Talk to specialist nurseries and seed merchants, before buying some marvel lous garden metalwork, and rounding off the day with a visit to the tearoom. This fair usually takes place in early May, but contact Holt Farm to confirm dates. Entry to this event is free, with a nominal fee for parking. Otherwise you can visit the farm visit on Thursdays, Fridays and the first Sunday of every month. **Call 01761 461650 or visit www.theorganicgardens.co.uk**

It made me laugh

Teacher: If you had a rabbit in a hutch, and you bought another rabbit, how many rabbits would you have?
Pupil: Tcn.
Teacher: You don't know your arithmetic.
Pupil: You don't know my rabbits.
Bill Reid, Salisbury, Wiltshire

Recipe of the week

Beetroot, Bacon and Cheddar Brunch Bread

Serves: 4
Preparation time: 20 minutes, plus 60–90 minutes proving
Cooking time: 25 minutes

250ml (8floz) warm water
1 tsp dried yeast
1 tsp sugar
500g (1lb) white bread flour
$^1/_2$ tsp salt
1 tsp dried sage (optional)
1 tbsp extra virgin olive oil
150g (5oz) plain, cooked, vacuum-packed beetroot, drained and puréed
5 rashers smoked streaky bacon
80g (3oz) mature cheddar, grated

1 Mix the water, yeast and sugar. After 5–10 minutes there should be a layer of foam on the surface.
2 Tip the flour into a large bowl, make a well in the centre and add the dried ingredients.
3 Pour in the water, yeast and beetroot then knead by hand for 10 minutes. Set aside to rise, until doubled in size.
4 Meanwhile, cook the bacon until crisp. Let cool, cut into pieces and set aside.
5 Turn the dough on to a floured work surface and roll into a large rectangle. Sprinkle bacon and cheese over then roll into a log. Tuck ends under, transfer to a baking sheet and set aside for 20 minutes to rise again. Preheat the oven to 220°C/425°F/Gas Mark 7.
6 Once the bread has risen, bake for around 25 minutes. When ready it should sound slightly hollow when tapped on the base.
© www.lovebeetroot.co.uk

11	Monday

12	Tuesday

13	Wednesday

14	Thursday

15	Friday

16	Saturday

17	Sunday

Seems like only yesterday

Doreen, aged ten, felt so proud being driven by her dad

Riding high

I was evacuated at the beginning of the war and was away from home for three years. When I returned I became a real daddy's girl. My Dad was a dustman. After serving in the First World War, he had found it hard to find work, so, with a wife and family to support, when he was offered the job he was only too pleased to take it – especially as it meant being taught to drive.

Like many people in those days, Dad came home every day for his midday meal. After dropping off his mate, he would drive down a long straight road before turning into our street. It was my joy, whenever possible, to go and wait for him at the top of the road. When he saw me standing there he would pull over and I would climb up into the passenger seat. Then he would drive me down the road, round the corner, and draw up at our house where he helped me down.

It didn't happen all that often because my being at school prevented it. But I don't think I have ever felt as proud in my life since I did those short trips, sitting up high on the dustcart, feeling better than anyone else in the world! I was very proud of my Dad.

Mrs Doreen Wyatt, Gravesend, Kent

It's a fact

In 1951 the American Humane Association decided that animals in films needed some recognition of their talents, and introduced the Picture Animal Top Star of the Year Award (PATSY). Its first winner was Francis the Talking Mule, who appeared in seven comedy films, who must have had star quality, as he went on to win again in 1952, 1954, 1955, 1956 and 1957.

Turn back time tips

Add grated fresh garlic to salad dressings to boost your immune system. Garlic and onions both contain compounds that could fight bacteria and viruses. Cooking them reduces their benefits so eat raw where you can.

Great days out

PIC: GARY HOLPIN

Bluebell Walks

South West Coastal Path
May is the perfect time for a coastal walk in the West Country, when the bluebells are truly breathtaking. Seasoned walkers should attempt the 12 or so miles from Salcome to Torcross, Devon, to see Salcombe's bluebell carpets (pictured). Other shorter walks include Cornwall's Helford Estuary, Brockholes in Exmoor and Langdon Hill, Dorset. **For more information about the area, advice on day trips and accommodation, visit www.southwestcoastpath.com/bluebellwalks**

It made me laugh

Q: Why did the banana go to the doctor?
A: Because it wasn't peeling very well.
Karen Booth, Peterborough, Cambridgeshire

Recipe of the week

Clementine Clouds

Serves: 6
Preparation time: 30 minutes, plus cooling
Cooking time: 5 minutes

3 large eggs, separated
100g (3^1/$_2$oz) caster sugar
2 tbsp clear honey
1 tbsp cornflour
250ml (8floz) freshly squeezed clementine juice (about 8 fruits)
Serving suggestions:
Thick double cream
Clementine slices
Shaved chocolate or chopped pistachios
Dessert biscuits

1 Beat the egg yolks with half the sugar until creamy and pale. Whisk in the honey and cornflour, then gradually whisk in the juice until evenly incorporated.
2 Transfer to a saucepan and stir regularly over low heat with a wooden spoon, until the mixture bubbles and thickens to a custard-like consistency. Cool in a bowl, stirring occasionally to prevent a skin forming.
3 In a separate bowl, whisk the egg whites until standing in soft peaks, then gradually whisk in the remaining sugar. Stir a large spoonful of the whites into the cooled mixture to soften it, before folding in the rest.
4 Spoon into serving glasses and chill until ready to serve. If liked, decorate with thick cream, clementine slices, shaved chocolate or chopped pistachios and dessert biscuits.
© www.budgens.co.uk

18 Monday

19 Tuesday

20 Wednesday

21 Thursday

22 Friday

23 Saturday

24 Sunday

Seems like only yesterday

The best of friends

As kids, Liz and I were best friends. Our favourite colour was green, we both liked sherbet lemons and had crushes on the same boys. I loved climbing trees, exploring and travelling to grandma's upstairs on the double-decker bus. Those were the things that were important to me.

Liz fancied being married to Mr Pollard, the solicitor who lived near our school. "That's what I want when I'm grown up," she breathed as we passed Mrs Pollard clad in a fur coat and jaunty hat getting into a Jaguar. Liz spread out her grubby hands and said: "I'm going to have a different ring for each finger when I'm married to a solicitor!"

When the results of the 11-plus exam arrived, my mum's hands were shaking as the opened the envelope. I asked: "Have I passed?" and she replied: "Of course you have!" her eyes sparkling with tears. Liz had not passed and said airily: "Mum says grammar school is for snobs. Suppose you don't want to be friends no more?"

She tossed her head and looked at me from the corner of her eye. I caught her hand: "Don't be daft! We'll always be friends!" Her face lit up and we skipped down the road together.

I didn't see anything of Liz for years and then one day she appeared in the town centre. She climbed out of a Jaguar wearing a fur coat, killer heels and a hat set at a jaunty angle…

Helen Davies, Congleton, Cheshire

It's a fact

It's no secret that film stars often change their names, but did you know that Dean Martin started life as Dino Crocetti? Cary Grant's original moniker was Archibald Leach, while Jane Seymour's was Joyce Frankenberger, Doris Day's was Doris von Kappelhoff and Kirk Douglas was Issur Danielovitch.

Turn back time tips

Sip mint tea to calm indigestion; just pour boiling water over two teaspoons of fresh mint in a cup and leave to infuse for a few minutes. Drink little and often after a meal.

Great days out

Open Garden Weekend

Canterbury Cathedral, Kent, May 24-25
Thanks to the National Garden Scheme, the Cathedral's private gardens are open to the public for just one weekend a year – so don't miss out! And, of course, there's the small matter of one of the UK's most famous buildings to explore. Combined Cathedral & Garden tickets are available from the Christ Church Gate, however, final details and dates await confirmation. **Call 01227 762862 or visit www.canterbury-cathedral.org**

It made me laugh

Sean and Mary had been saving up to go on holiday. One day, Sean came home and announced he had bought a boat! Mary was not pleased so, to stop her nagging, he said she could choose the boat's name. At last, the big day came to launch the boat, and Mary revealed her chosen name: 'For Sale'.

Dorothy Bloor, Leek, Staffordshire

Recipe of the week

Fiery Chicken Pasta

Serves: 4
Cooking time: 15 minutes
Preparation time: 5 minutes

250g (8oz) asparagus
4-5 chicken thighs, cut into 6 pieces
100g (3^{1}/$_{2}$oz) smoked pancetta or bacon, cubed
3-4 shallots, sliced
2 cloves garlic, crushed
1 green chilli, finely chopped or 1 tsp chilli powder to taste
1 tbsp rosemary, very finely chopped
400g tin chopped tomatoes
1 tsp sugar
Salt and pepper
300g (10oz) dried spaghetti pasta
50g (2oz) Parmesan cheese, grated

1 Trim the ends of the asparagus then chop the spears into 4-5 pieces.
2 Fry the chicken for 5-6 minutes in a hot pan with some oil then add the pancetta, shallots, garlic, chilli and rosemary and cook over medium heat for a further 3-4 minutes.
3 Add the asparagus and chopped tomatoes then simmer for another 3-4 minutes. Season with salt, pepper and sugar.
4 Meanwhile, cook the pasta according to packet instructions, drain and add to the sauce. Grate Parmesan over the dish before serving.
© www.british-asparagus.co.uk

25 Monday

26 Tuesday

27 Wednesday

28 Thursday

29 Friday

30 Saturday

31 Sunday

Seems like only yesterday

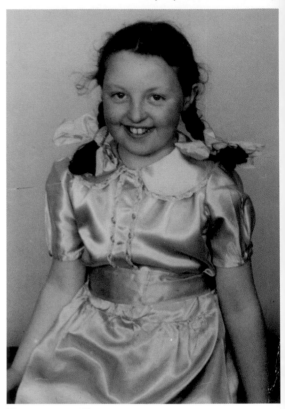

Toys are still us

I was born in 1941. As it was wartime, there weren't many toys to buy in the shops so Dad made me toys, which I loved. Some of the things he made were a dolls' house with lights in every room powered by a little battery, a monkey on a stick and a parrot that rocked up and down on the edge of a table. Mum knitted toys for me. I remember Red Riding Hood and the three bears, but my favourite was a large Minnie Mouse which she hung on my bedroom door, as a surprise, one Christmas morning.

In the Sixties, I knitted toys for my own children. Later, I was given a Jean Greenhowe book of patterns for toys so I started knitting them to raise money for charity. I sold them at local school fêtes and over the years I have seen children grow up and bring their own children along. Wishing to help animals in need, I recently decided to make little donkeys. I made 600 and sent them to horse and donkey sanctuaries to sell in their visitors' shops. As I buy all the wool and stuffing for the toys from charity shops, that also contributes to good causes.

Every year my daughter gives me Jean Greenhowe patterns for Christmas, Easter, my birthday and Mothers' Day so I hope to carry on knitting for many years to come.

Mrs Diane Clarke, Yate, Bristol

It's a fact

East Peckham in Kent has a unique claim to fame: it's where the first-ever speeding ticket was issued, in January 1896. Walter Arnold was spotted driving at 8mph in a 2mph zone, but was easily apprehended by a policeman riding a bicycle, and fined one shilling – how times have changed!

Turn back time tips

Plain natural yogurt makes a great and low cost occasional facemask. It's perfect in summer for cooling skin and also contains lactic acid, a form of alpha hydroxy that's found in lots of skincare products and helps dissolve dead skin cells. The gentle exfoliating action smoothes dry skin leaving it brighter and more hydrated.

Great days out

Holker Garden Festival

Holker Hall, Cumbria, May 29-31
Whether you're looking for gardening tips, tasty artisan produce, or country crafts, you'll find it at Holker. Show gardens, perfectly-perfumed marquees of flowers, and even sheepdog displays will keep you busy until the sun goes down. The beautiful Lake District setting is unforgettable, plus Grange-over-Sands is just a stone's throw away. **For further information or to buy advance tickets visit www.holkerfestival.co.uk or call 01539 558838.**

It made me laugh

A ghost walks into a pub and asks for a whisky. "Sorry," says the landlord, "we don't serve spirits."
Angela Drummond, Woking, Surrey

Recipe of the week

Fluffy Lime Puddings

Serves: 6
Preparation time: 20 minutes
Cooking time: 20 minutes

50g (2oz) butter
250g (8oz) caster sugar
3 eggs, separated
75g (3oz) plain flour
300ml (½pt) milk
Finely grated zest and juice of 2 limes
Icing sugar, for dusting

1 Preheat the oven to 180°C/350°F/Gas Mark 4.
2 Beat the butter in a large bowl until soft and creamy. Add the sugar and beat until pale and fluffy. Add the egg yolks one at a time, beating each one in before adding the next.
3 Sift in the flour and add the milk, lime zest and juice, and mix well. The mixture will be quite liquid.
4 Whisk the egg whites in a large, clean bowl until they form stiff peaks. Gently fold into the cake mixture then divide between six ramekins or ovenproof teacups.
5 Arrange on a baking sheet and place in the oven. Bake for 15–20 minutes or until just set. Remove and cool slightly before dusting with icing sugar and serving.
© www.facebook.com/KerrygoldUK

1 Monday

2 Tuesday

3 Wednesday

4 Thursday

5 Friday

6 Saturday

7 Sunday

Seems like only yesterday

Margaret, right, enjoyed her school days in the cookery class

When girls were girls!

As I failed the 11-plus exam, I attended Wesley Street Secondary Modern school in the village of Farsley. Our teachers were strict and if we stepped out of line we had to report to the headmaster's study. Nearby was the sick room where periodically we would queue to see the nurse for 'nit inspection'.

Domestic Science was taught only to girls. We made delicious shepherd's pies, Cornish pasties as well as meat-and-potato pies topped with shortcrust or puff pastry. For 'afters' we made Victoria sponge cakes, scones, apple pies and lemon meringue pies. The importance of safety and hygiene in the kitchen was instilled in us. We learned how to care for our hands and fingernails as well as how to clean our face thoroughly with soap and water to prevent blackheads.

On occasions we stayed in the cookery room at lunchtime unattended by the teacher. Disorder would ensue. Soggy dishcloths and tea-towels screwed up into balls were hurled across the room at one another. Small balls of bread dough made excellent missiles. Before our unsuspecting teacher returned, order was restored. Dishcloths and tea-towels were put through the mangle several times to squeeze out excess water then neatly hung up to dry so the room looked spick and span.

Happy days when girls would be girls!

Margaret Humphries, Leeds

It's a fact

Llyn Tegid (known as Bala Lake) in Gwynedd, Wales, is home to a rare type of whitefish called the gwyniad, which is found nowhere else on the planet. It's thought its ancestors were trapped in the waters there at the end of the last Ice Age.

Turn back time tips

Don't rule out cropped or Capri-pants but choose wisely because wide-leg styles can shorten the legs and make you look frumpy. Instead stick to slim-fitting styles and pick ones that finish at the slimmest point whether it's slightly below your calves or just above. Wear with a heel or wedge to lengthen the legs.

Great days out

Pentillie Castle Garden Tours

Saltash, Cornwall
Take a guided tour with a member of the Coryton family, who manage this boutique Bed and Breakfast, or turn up for one of the spring Garden Open Days to explore Sir James Tillie's hidden vault for yourself! Tour and Open Day dates are unconfirmed at time of press, but private garden tours can also be arranged, inclusive of afternoon tea. **Call 01579 350044 or visit www.pentille.co.uk to arrange.**

It made me laugh

A police patrol car is overtaken by a car driven at high speed by a woman busy knitting. The police officer lowers his window and shouts: "Pull over!" The woman shakes her head and yells back: "No... socks!"
Mr D Woodhead, via email

Recipe of the week

Pasta with Butter Grilled Asparagus and Parma Ham

Serves: 6
Preparation time: 30 minutes
Cooking time: 10 minutes

500g (1lb 2oz) 00 or strong white bread flour
1 tsp salt
4 eggs
20 spears asparagus
75g (3oz) butter
3 tbsp crème fraîche
8 large slices Parma or Serrano ham, cut into strips
Salt and pepper
Parmesan shavings, grated lemon zest and basil leaves, to garnish

1 Add the flour and salt to a large bowl. Whisk the eggs, then add two thirds to the flour and knead for 5 minutes to form dough (add more egg if necessary). Rest for 10 minutes, before rolling out to 1mm thick. Cut into strips about 1cm wide and dust with flour. Set aside.
2 Remove and discard the bottom of each asparagus spear. Place a griddle pan over high heat.
3. Spread half the butter over the asparagus. Cook for 3-4 minutes each side, cut into pieces and toss with remaining butter.
4 Boil a pan of salted water. Cook pasta for 2-4 minutes until al dente. Drain, reserving a few tbsp of cooking liquid, and return to the pan, off the heat.
5 Add the crème fraîche to the pasta and toss to coat. Add asparagus, ham and seasoning. Serve with Parmesan, lemon zest and basil.

Top Tip: Not an asparagus fan? Use thinly sliced courgettes instead.
© www.facebook.com/KerrygoldUK

8 Monday

9 Tuesday

10 Wednesday

11 Thursday

12 Friday

13 Saturday

14 Sunday

Seems like only yesterday

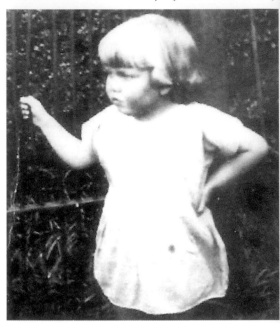

Steeped in history

I feel very proud that my grandparents' old home, the dower house for Douglas Castle, is now the Douglas Heritage Museum, housing memorabilia from local people as well as the history of this fascinating village.

From April to September I work as a guide in the museum and every time I am on duty I recall scenes from the past. I can still see the old dresser where Granny's bottle of wintergreen stood on a shelf. Its strong smell mingles with the aroma of Granddad's Erinmore tobacco. And the delicious smell of scones and pancakes made on the griddle still seems to pervade the place.

As a child I was a regular visitor and have many happy memories, including the time I accidentally dropped Granny's false teeth from the jam jar into the old stone sink while I was washing up. She just smiled a gappy smile and said: "Don't worry, lass – naebody'll be looking at me!"

I remember Granddad standing by the same sink to wash with water that Granny had heated in a huge kettle swinging over an equally huge fire. Sometimes I walked alongside the Douglas Water to meet him coming home from work in the coal mine. He would give me a jam sandwich kept back especially for me. I felt I'd been given gold!

Many centuries before me there had been a famous visitor to my grandparents' home. In 1565 Mary Queen of Scots stayed there with her husband, Lord Darnley, who was related to the Douglas family.

Christina Gibbs, Douglas, Lanarkshire

It's a fact

A cave in Aberystwyth was once home to the Crown jewels. They were moved into a library there from 1939 up until 1945 to protect them from German bombs, along with a copy of the Magna Carta, drawings by Leonardo da Vinci, Scott's Antarctic journals and other valuable documents.

Turn back time tips

If you're in pain try listening to music, research has found that listening to your favourite song could help to ease pain and discomfort. Simon and Garfunkel's Bridge Over Troubled Water is the most comforting apparently.

Great days out

Chatsworth House

Bakewell, Derbyshire
This 105-acre Peak District estate is simply stunning in summer. The spectacular hillside water feature is perfect for paddling, and the rooms are light and airy if you need to get out of the sun. We loved spotting the various links to Marie Antoinette – who was a friend of Georgiana Spencer Cavendish, Chatsworth's 18th century Duchess. **Call 01246 565300 or visit www. chatsworth.org**

It made me laugh

A man took his pet crocodile with him to watch a film at the cinema. "I didn't think I'd ever see a crocodile in here watching the film!" said the usher. "Neither did I," said the man, "he hated the book."

David Evans, Cardiff

Recipe of the week

Strawberry Cream Victoria Sponge Cake

Serves: 4
Preparation time: 20 minutes
Baking time: 20 minutes

175g (6oz) butter, soft
175g (6oz) caster sugar
3 fresh eggs
175g (6oz) self-raising flour
250ml (8floz) double cream
1 tsp vanilla bean paste, or vanilla extract
1 tbsp icing sugar and extra for sifting
400g (13oz) strawberries
4 tbsp strawberry jam (optional)

1 Pre-heat the oven to 180°C350°F/Gas Mark 4. Butter and line two 18cm (8in) sandwich tins with baking parchment.
2 Beat the butter and sugar till pale and fluffy. Add the eggs, one at a time, beating well. Fold in the flour, one spoon at a time.
3 Divide mixture between tins and bake for 20 minutes until risen, golden and firm.
4 Cool the sponges on a wire rack. Hull the strawberries and slice in half. Whip the cream till quite stiff, mixing in the icing sugar and the vanilla.
5 When cool, spread jam on one of the sponge cakes (if using), plus half the whipped cream on top. Place half of the strawberries on top of the cream. Top with the other sponge cake and spread with remaining whipped cream. Arrange remaining strawberries around the cake.
© www.sweetevestrawberries.co.uk

June 15 - 21

15 Monday

16 Tuesday

17 Wednesday

18 Thursday

19 Friday

20 Saturday

21 Sunday

Seems like only yesterday

Wedding day finery

This photo was taken in the Sixties at the wedding of my favourite uncle. He was (still is) a larger-than-life character who was always on the go and – more important to us kids – always used to turn up with quarter bags of sweets which were a great treat.

I was aged around three and a half when he got married and was forced to wear a blue corduroy and waistcoat combo and (worst of all) a bow tie. I think the look on my face says it all! Actually, I think I probably got off fairly lightly as my older sister was a bridesmaid and had to wear a bright orange satin dress that I am sure she would be horrified to be seen in today.

I am being escorted by my very fashionable mother wearing a trendy hat and behind us are my Scottish great aunts who I am sure were only there to prevent my escape! I believe they were called Flora and Tina and they always reminded me of the fairies in the Walt Disney film, Sleeping Beauty.

When I see this photo now, I look back on all the wonderful people, both family and friends, that attended the wedding and feel sad to think how many are no longer with us. Thank goodness for old photographs that help us to keep our memories of them all alive.

Chris Munden, Donington, Lincs

It's a fact

They may be a symbol of our national identity but, in fact, the seaside delicacy of fish and chips stems from several other cultures. The chips are a descendent of the French fry, while deep-fried battered fish was first popularised by Jewish refugees from Portugal and Spain in the 1800s. Still, we were the first to combine the two!

Turn back time tips

Our brows help frame our eyes and give our face definition, but as we age they thin and become straggly so need a little extra attention. Have your brows shaped occasionally by a professional and they'll help you find the best brow shape for your features. When tidying them up remove one hair at a time and remember less is more.

Great days out

Easton Walled Gardens

Nr Grantham, Lincolnshire
Fancy some peace and quiet? How about the 'lost' gardens of Easton? The site is more than 400 years old but has only been restored since the beginning of the 21st century, after the estate house fell into disrepair and was demolished. It's astonishing how much beautiful work has been done, not only in the main garden, but also the vegetable garden, cottage garden and Pickery. You might find us in the tearoom, though. **Call 01476 530063 or visit www.eastonwalledgardens.co.uk**

It made me laugh

I took my nephew to the shops and asked him: "Do you want blue cheese?" He replied: "Why, are there any blue cows?"

Irene Woodcock, Dukinfield, Tameside

Recipe of the week

Roasted Beetroot, Carrot, Feta and Quinoa Salad

Serves: 4
Preparation time: 10 minutes
Cooking time: 30 minutes

4 raw beetroot, peeled and cut into large chunks
150g (5oz) baby carrots, with tops washed
4 tbsp olive oil
1 tsp cumin seeds
250g (8oz) quinoa
200g (7oz) feta cheese, cubed
1 bag baby salad leaves
Dressing:
200g (7oz) Greek-style lemon yogurt
1 tbsp white wine vinegar
1 tbsp wholegrain mustard
30g (1oz) runny honey
1 tsp cumin seeds
1 tsp ground cumin
Salt and pepper

1 Preheat the oven to 200°C/400°F/Gas Mark 6. Toss the beetroot and carrots in olive oil and roast in a baking tray with cumin seeds for 30 minutes until soft.
2 Cook the quinoa according to packet instructions, drain, and leave to cool.
3 Whisk together all the dressing ingredients.
4 Mix the quinoa with the roasted beetroot, baby carrots and cooking juices and add the feta cubes. Add the dressing and toss well.
5 Serve on a bed of baby salad leaves, either alone or with crusty bread.
© www.rachelsorganic.co.uk

June 22 - 28

22 Monday

23 Tuesday

24 Wednesday

25 Thursday

26 Friday

27 Saturday

28 Sunday

Seems like only yesterday

Thank you, Mum

This photo of me with my mother was taken when I was aged sixteen. As my father had been badly wounded in the First World War and my parents were adamant that they would not accept charity, she worked all hours to put food on the table and pay the rent.

The early years of my life were spent with my mother while she was cleaning the homes of wealthy people. The people she worked for were very kind and they all made a fuss of me. One elderly Jewish lady always insisted that my mother had a mid-morning break when she would give me Matzo bead with Edam cheese. She also took delight in keeping a check on my height as I grew up.

Every Sunday my mother took me to church where my older brother was in the choir. I used to ask if I could join, but was told that I had to wait until I was six. Soon the big day arrived; I loved every minute of it, dressed in cassock, collar and surplice, and stayed for 11 years.

Our area was heavily bombed in the London Blitz and the few of us that weren't evacuated spent most of our lessons in the bomb shelter. Despite this I passed the scholarship exam to go to grammar school. Although we were too poor to buy the school uniform, I felt very proud and enjoyed finding out that I was also good at cricket and football.

Mr G Carter, Easingwold, York

It's a fact

The windiest place on Earth is Port Martin, in Antarctica, where winds average more than 40mph on at least 100 days every year. The place with the least wind is also in Antarctica, at a site called Dome A – a much easier destination to put up an umbrella!

Turn back time tips

If you're going for a stay in hospital have a probiotic drink every day before you. It could help to build up your immunity and protect you from hospital bugs and infections.

Great days out

Barnsdale Gardens

Exton, Rutland
Home to Britain's largest collection of individually-designed gardens, Barnsdale was also once the home of the BBC's Gardeners' World, so you might recognise it! It's open all year round, with reduced rates in winter – but at this time of year there's plenty going on in the Nursery, plus various seasonal courses and events which have previously included cookery demonstrations, First World War-themed days, rural crafts and even wildlife events. **Call 01572 813200 or visit www.barnsdalegardens.co.uk**

It made me laugh

In bed one night, my wife turned to me and said: "My memory isn't getting any better."
"Why, what have you forgotten now?" I asked.
"Well, nothing," she replied. "It's just these new pillows I bought said they were Improved Memory Pillows, but I haven't noticed a difference."
Words failed me!
Mr A K Howard, Hull East Yorkshire

Recipe of the week

Date and Pistachio bars

Serves: 12
Preparation time: 15 minutes
Cooking time: 20 minutes

100g (3½oz) honey
100g (3½oz) oats
100g (3½oz) pistachios roughly chopped
1 tbsp rapeseed oil
1 tsp flaxseeds
1 tsp psyllium husk (or just use extra flaxseeds)
50g (2oz) dried dates, roughly chopped
20g (2oz) golden raisins

1 Preheat your oven to 180°C/350°F/Gas Mark 4. Lined a 20cm (9in) baking tray with greaseproof paper.
2 Mix all ingredients in a large bowl. Place the mixture on the baking tray and flatten with a wooden spoon. Cover with baking paper and place another baking tray on top, then gently push down to completely flatten the mixture. Don't apply too much pressure or the bars will come out too hard.
3 Remove the extra tray and paper and bake for 20 minutes.
4 Remove from the oven and let cool completely. Slice into bars and serve.
Top tip: These will keep in an airtight jar for 10 days.
© www.detoxkitchen.co.uk

29 Monday

30 Tuesday

1 Wednesday

2 Thursday

3 Friday

4 Saturday

5 Sunday

Seems like only yesterday

My car, my pal

In the Eighties I bought my first car, a yellow Citroen 2CV6. It had a certain charm all of its own – very versatile in design and built for adventure. I loved it for its style as well as its colour.

I remember one occasion when a friend asked if I could help her transport two goats from her smallholding to a farm a few miles away. As the seats were removable, I was able to take the back ones out and in went the goats, quite happily. All four of us arrived at our destination without a problem.

One December, I decided to buy a six-foot Christmas tree and my 2CV came to the rescue again. I peeled back the canvas roof and the tree sat securely in the car on its journey home. Fortunately, I escaped the eyes (and the CCTV cameras) of the law as I don't think a car with a fir tree protruding from its roof would have met with police approval!

My yellow companion and I were inseparable for a number of years and we went on to get in and out of many scrapes together. Indeed, it helped me to gain my independence following the breakdown of a long-term relationship, proving that the Deux Chevaux, as the French call it, is not just a car, it's a way of life.

Miss Carol Ann Massey, Ceres, Fife

It made me laugh

Q: Why shouldn't you marry a tennis player?
A: Because love means nothing to them.
Lorraine Foster, via email

It's a fact

If you visit Japan in February, don't expect to receive sweets from your sweetheart! On February 14th it's only women who purchase Valentine's chocolate for their other halves, and the favour isn't returned until a month later, on White Day – the male version – on March 14th. Far too long to wait for pralines, in our opinion!

Turn back time tips

Olive oil is a purse-friendly beauty secret that most of us will have in our kitchen cupboards. A good source of Vitamins A and E, olive oil is great for all-over hydration, particularly on common dry spots such as knees and elbows. It's also a brilliant multi-tasking wrinkle buster, makes a great face massage oil and is handy for removing make-up.

Great days out

PIC. NATIONAL TRUST

Birmingham Back to Backs

Hurst Street and Inge Street
These are Birmingham's last surviving back-to-backs; literally where two streets met around a communal courtyard. The houses themselves have been carefully restored, and a guided tour will take you from the 1840s through to the 1970s, with insights into the lives of past residents. Craft sessions are available on various dates, plus they're looking for volunteers – so who knows, you might get hooked… Visits are by appointment only, and booking is essential. **Call 01216 667671 or visit www. nationaltrust.org.uk/birmingham-back-to-backs**

Recipe of the week

Sweet and Savoury Pork Stir-Fry

Serves: 6
Preparation time: 20 minutes
Cooking time: 30 minutes

275ml (9floz) goat's milk or single cream
50ml (2floz) fish sauce
1 tbsp garlic cooking paste
2 star anise
$^{3}/_{4}$ tsp black pepper
$^{1}/_{4}$ tsp Chinese five spice
125g (4oz) sugar
75ml (3floz) water
3 tbsp sunflower oil
1 onion, thinly sliced
675g (1lb6oz) pork tenderloin, cut into thin slices
450g (14oz) jasmine rice, cooked according to pack directions

1 Mix the milk or cream, fish sauce, garlic paste, star anise, pepper and spice in a medium bowl and set aside. Bring sugar and water to the boil over medium heat. Cook for 10-12 minutes, until golden brown, then carefully whisk in the milk mixture until sugar is dissolved, then set aside.
2 Heat 2 tbsp oil in large pan over medium–high heat. Add the pork in batches and brown on both sides. Remove all from pan; add remaining oil with the onion and fry for 5 minutes, stirring occasionally until browned.
3 Stir in your caramel sauce, cooking for 5 minutes over medium heat. Return the pork to the pan to heat through. Serve over cooked rice.
© www.schwartz.co.uk/recipes

6 Monday

7 Tuesday

8 Wednesday

9 Thursday

10 Friday

11 Saturday

12 Sunday

Seems like only yesterday

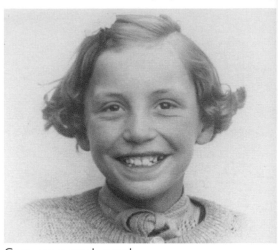

Sun, sea and sand

I have a blissful childhood memory of one day when I was eight years old on holiday in Mablethorpe. The day was warm and sunny, the blue sky rivalling the blue sea. The gentle lap of the waves caressed the soft sand, filling the naturally formed rock pools with deep warm seawater. Crabs, shellfish and silvery fish darted in and out of the rocks at the clear bottom of the pool.

I was happily splashing in the rock pool when suddenly I realised that I had managed to swim one perfect breaststroke. Then I sank. I rushed tripping across the sand dunes as I called out to my mother: "I can swim!"

Ours wasn't the seaside of donkey rides, ice cream and Punch & Judy shows but one of gritty sandwiches, wide horizons, silver sands and very few people. As the sun slipped over the horizon, we went back to my grandparents' Lincolnshire farm, sunburnt and hungry.

On the farm, I helped my mother and her sisters to churn the milk for butter-making. With my brothers, I collected eggs from the hen house and scoured the hedgerows to seek out eggs hidden in the ditches by wily chickens. I remember bringing the cows in from the fields to the milking sheds. Those were days of freedom and endless sunshine and the sweet, musty scent of hay in the barns.

Pat Parnell, Dorchester, Dorset

It made me laugh

While I was watching TV, my four-year-old son clambered on to the sofa and began to play with my hair. When I asked what he was doing he replied: "I'm looking for the eyes in the back of your head!"

Mrs S Beecroft, Ipswich, Suffolk

It's a fact

During her reign the Queen has received many unusual gifts including a variety of live animals. The less palace-friendly animals have been placed in the care of London Zoo, among them jaguars and sloths from Brazil, and two black beavers from Canada. The Queen has also received gifts of pineapples, eggs, a box of snail shells, a grove of maple trees and 7kg of prawns.

Turn back time tips

Don't forget to floss – the bacteria that cause gum disease could also contribute to your risk of heart disease or dementia. Try to floss every day – especially in the evening to move all traces of food.

Great days out

Forties Weekend

Black Country Living Museum, Dudley, West Midlands

For a right rip-roaring weekend, plus a night out on the tiles, head down to meet fellow spivs and canary girls in wartime Britain. Dress to impress or simply experience Forties life, plus evening entertainment that is so popular that your ticket must be pre-booked. Do the jitterbug and take home some ripping memorabilia! Usually takes place mid-July with dates subject to change. **For tickets and further information, call 01215 579643 or visit www.bclm.com**

Recipe of the week

Blueberry and Lavender Cake

Serves: 12
Preparation time: 90 minutes
Cooking time: 25 minutes

175g (6oz) unsalted butter
175g (6oz) caster sugar
3 eggs
1 tsp vanilla extract
225g (7½oz) self-raising flour
150g (5oz) low-fat natural yogurt
150g (5oz) blueberries
Syrup:
60g (2¼ oz) caster sugar
40ml (1¾floz) water
3 sprigs fresh lavender
Icing:
250g (8oz) unsalted butter
750g (1½lb) icing sugar
75g (3oz) fat-free blueberry yogurt
Drop of milk
2 tsp violet food colouring
Fresh lavender or lavender sugar

1 Grease and line three 15cm (6in) cake tins. Preheat oven to 170°C/325°F/Gas Mark 3.
2 Cream the butter and sugar until pale and fluffy. Whisk in the eggs individually, add vanilla extract and flour, then fold in yogurt and blueberries.
4 Pour into the tins and bake until risen, golden and springy. Transfer to a wire rack and cool completely before removing.
5 Simmer all the syrup ingredients over high heat for 5 minutes, then let cool.
6 For the icing, beat butter and icing sugar into a paste. Add yogurt, plus milk if too stiff. Beat in food colouring.
7 Place the first cake on your serving plate. Drizzle with syrup, then spread icing over. Repeat with second and third cakes.
8 Ice top and sides. Decorate with lavender or lavender sugar.
© www.rachelsorganic.co.uk

13 Monday

14 Tuesday

15 Wednesday

16 Thursday

17 Friday

18 Saturday

19 Sunday

Seems like only yesterday

Happy campers

In the Fifties our family was very fortunate to have a motorbike and sidecar. Dad was a founder member of the Bradford Central Sidecar Club and whatever the weather – rain, shine or even snow – we spent most Sundays out with the club.

We visited the Yorkshire Dales, Derbyshire, the east coast and Sherwood Forest and caused quite a stir in the villages as thirty of us drove through. On arrival at our destination, a circle like a wagon train was formed. The younger children played inside the circle while the older ones went off to explore. We paddled in the streams, played cricket and rounders, and in Sherwood Forest we played hide and seek in the famous big oak before it was cordoned off. In winter, we had hot stew warmed up on a primus stove. A real treat in our annual calendar was Children's Day held at Shipley Glen when each of us was given 2s 6d in threepenny bits to spend at the local amusements.

We also enjoyed camping holidays. Mum used to save all year to pay for the petrol and camp fees. Each week she would put by an extra tin of food and Dad would laugh at the weight of it, but managed to pack it all in anyway. We didn't have any money to spend (except for ice cream) but we had buckets and spades and lots of fun and games. Such fond memories!

Ann Swain, Ferrybridge, W Yorkshire

It made me laugh

Q: What did the water say to the wine?
A: I'm diluted to meet you.

Lauren Brown, Cambridge

It's a fact

Every day, more money is printed for family-favourite board game Monopoly than for the US Treasury. The company that owns monopoly, Parker Brothers, prints about $50 billion of Monopoly money every year – enough to buy a real hotel on Park Lane!

Turn back time tips

If you need a belt to help keep up your trousers, then you're wearing the wrong size! Instead a belt is a great way of finishing off a look or when worn at the waist, it's a quick way to reclaim your waist and create curves. Add yours over a dress or jacket to give it shape and don't be afraid to try colourful styles.

Great days out

Battle Proms

Hatfield House, Hertfordshire, Jul 18
Feeling patriotic? Must be Proms time, then! In a setting renowned for its beautiful gardens, come and watch stunning aerial displays, cavalry demonstrations with canon fire and phenomenal fireworks – all set to the fabulous music of the Battle Proms. It's the perfect way to see a summer afternoon into evening, at this Jacobean gem of a house. Gates open 4.30pm. **Call 01707 287010 or visit www.hatfieldhouse.co.uk**

Recipe of the week

Chilli Tacos with Homemade Guacamole and Salsa

Serves: 4-6
Preparation time: 1 hour
Cooking time: 1 hour

500g (1lb) minced beef
2 onions, chopped
2 cloves garlic, finely chopped
Chilli powder, to taste
2 tsp ground cumin
1 tsp each ground coriander and cinnamon
3 tbsp tomato purée
2 beef stock cubes
300ml ($1/2$pt) water
Bay leaf
Salt and pepper
400g can tinned tomatoes
400g can red kidney beans
400g can baked beans
Taco shells and grated cheese
Guacamole:
Flesh of 3 ripe avocados
2 fresh green and 2 fresh red chillies
2 tomatoes, deseeded and chopped
Red onion, finely chopped
Handful fresh coriander
Salt to taste
Juice of 1 lime
80g ($3^1/4$oz) low-fat natural yogurt
Salsa:
2 large tomatoes, deseeded and finely chopped
Small red onion, finely chopped
Small bunch coriander, finely chopped
2 mild green chillies, chopped
Juice of 1 lime

1 Fry mince and onions over medium heat, until meat is cooked and onions soft.
2 Add the garlic, chilli, spices, purée and stock cubes. Stir-fry for 2 minutes.
3 Add water, bay leaf, tomatoes and seasoning. Simmer for 40 minutes, stirring occasionally. Add all beans and cook for another 20 minutes.
4 Make condiments by blending or mixing all ingredients
5 Fill tacos with chilli, sprinkle with cheese and serve with condiments.
© www.rachelsorganic.co.uk

20 Monday

21 Tuesday

22 Wednesday

23 Thursday

24 Friday

25 Saturday

26 Sunday

Seems like only yesterday

Comics and fizzy pop

No matter how little money we had, our parents always made sure had two weeks away in the summer. When we were very small, this would usually mean a camping holiday with our grandparents. I often wonder how my mother coped with catering for seven of us in a tent. One year, she had three children aged under five and two in nappies (and this was in the days before disposable nappies).

Dad must also have had saint-like patience to put up with small children crammed in the back of the car. It must have been difficult to drive with us squabbling and asking: "Are we there yet?" There were no seat belts so we would swap places, climbing over one another. An old ice-cream tub was provided in case anyone was travel sick.

But we had plenty of fun. Granddad used to give us money to spend on seaside toys and we were given comics to read (which I now suspect was a way to let the grown ups have five minutes' peace). We also got to sit in beer gardens with bottles of dandelion and burdock pop and maybe a packet of Smiths Salt 'n' Shake crisps. The smell of bacon frying brings back fond memories of those childhood holidays.

One very hot summer Nan finally gave in and bought a sun hat. That night there was an almighty thunderstorm and the weather changed for the worse. After that Nan always teasingly claimed it was her sun hat that had made the sun go away.

Tracy Munden, Donnington, Lincolnshire

It's a fact

In 1941 the crew of the HMS Trident submarine lived for six weeks with a reindeer called Pollyanna on board – gifted to them by the Russians. She slept under the captain's bed, drank condensed milk, and ate a navigation chart. She was brought on to the submarine through a torpedo tube – but on returning to Britain, she'd put on so much weight, she wouldn't fit in the tube and had to be winched out.

Turn back time tips

Sip soup for weight loss. Soup fills you up for very few calories. Make it the main event of your lunch or choose it as a starter and you'll eat less of your main course.

Great days out

Trentham Gardens and Estate

Stoke-on-Trent, Staffordshire
Hurrah for the restoration crew that lovingly revived Trentham just over 10 years ago. Not only is it home to one of the most visited gardens in the country, but just next door is the most beautiful Scandinavian-style shopping street of wooden cabins, plus a substantial garden centre. You can also take a boat trip across the lake, or even branch out on the 'barefoot trail' for a few surprises! **Call 01782 646646 or visit www.trentham.co.uk**

It made me laugh

I am 65 and walk with a Zimmer frame. Having just heard the good news that the country was about to welcome a royal baby, I got into a taxi and, with a huge smile, said to the young taxi driver: "So, we're having a baby then!" Needless to say he looked a little alarmed!

Linda Hardcastle, Lowestoft, Suffolk

Recipe of the week

Raspberry Iced Dessert

Serves: 4
Preparation time: 20 minutes

250g (8oz) frozen raspberries
200g (7oz) soft cheese
100g (3½oz) natural or Greek yogurt
Grated rind of 1 lemon and 1–2 tsp lemon juice
50g (2oz) icing sugar, sieved (optional)
Fresh mint leaves to decorate (optional)

1 Place the raspberries, reserving a few for decoration, in a bowl and leave for 15 minutes.
2 In a separate large bowl, beat the soft cheese until smooth. Stir in the yogurt, lemon juice (not rind), and icing sugar, if used.
3 Add the raspberries and mix until combined and marbled with pink stripes.
4 Transfer to individual serving glasses and top with reserved raspberries, grated lemon rind, and mint leaves if desired.

Top tip: try swapping the icing sugar for honey
© www.coolcookery.co.uk

27 Monday

28 Tuesday

29 Wednesday

30 Thursday

31 Friday

1 Saturday

2 Sunday

Seems like only yesterday

Festival fun

I was brought up in Portsmouth and this photo was taken in the summer of 1951 when we had our Festival of Britain street party. My younger brother Frank is on the left at the front, dressed as a jester, and I am next to him as Red Riding Hood. The blonde lady behind me is our mother, Nora.

There were so many street parties held at that time there was a run on fancy dress costumes from a local shop called U-Need-Us. A mere stone's throw from our school, it stocked everything needed for fun – jokes, magic tricks and party favours to brighten those austere post-war years.

I loved the magic tricks and also used to buy sheets of crêpe paper that I used for various craft projects. Frank loved the joke items such as black face soap, stink bombs and itching powder, all of which featured in the popular children's comics of the day. He once bought a revoltingly realistic 'mucky pup' joke and our parents dutifully went through the motions (no pun intended) of expressing shock and horror even though the only pets we had were goldfish.

The name U-Need-Us passed into popular folklore with expressions such as 'I'll give you a thick ear from U-Need-Us' being used as a jocular threat. Founded as long ago as 1923, thankfully, U-Need-Us is still in existence. Long may it continue to provide harmless fun for generations to come!

Mary Cook, Market Rasen, Lincs

It made me laugh

Q: What did Paddington Bear and Winnie the Pooh take on holiday?
A: The bear essentials.

Fiona Williams, Burnley, Lancashire

It's a fact

Most Muppets are left-handed. The reason for this is that most puppeteers are right-handed and operate the Muppet's head with their favoured hand, leaving the left one to control the arms. Muppets operated by more than one puppeteer, such as the Swedish Chef, are more likely to be right-handed.

Turn back time tips

Avoid powder foundations and matt formulas that will make your skin look flat and highlight your wrinkles. Choosing a light-reflecting foundation that gives a dewy finish will help your skin glow and look younger, plus it helps reflect light away from your skin helping to disguise any imperfections.

Great days out

Vintage & Modern Tours

The Cotswolds
Whether you're a walker, biker, vintage car fanatic or a lover of the open road, you've got to fit in a trip to the Cotswolds. These tours take in the sights and sounds across the area, from 'Va Va Vintage' to the north, 'Contemporary Cotswolds' to the south, 'Roman to Retro' in the east and the west's 'Retail Revival'. **Visit www.cotswoldvintagetours.com for lots more suggestions, tips and drivers' maps. We're off to download our free directions now!**

Recipe of the week

Brie and Mango Empanadas

Serves: 6
Preparation time: 20 minutes
Cooking time: 20 minutes

180g (6oz) unsalted butter
360g (12oz) plain flour
Large pinch salt
1 large egg, beaten
Filling:
1 fresh mango, diced
Pinch of salt and pepper
55g (2oz) diced red onion
1 tsp diced red chilli
1 tbsp coriander
100g (3¹/₂oz) Brie, diced
50g (2oz) Cheddar, grated
60g (2¹/₂oz) Red Leicester, grated
Salsa:
125ml (4floz) sweet chilli sauce
35g (1¹/₂oz) red pepper, diced
35g (1¹/₂oz) yellow pepper, diced
1 tbsp coriander
1 tbsp lime juice
35g (1¹/₂oz) red onion, diced
50g (2oz) sweetcorn kernels

1 Heat the oven to 180°C/350°F/Gas Mark 4, and melt the butter (set aside).
2 Mix the dry empanada ingredients then add the wet, plus 3-5 tbsp water, to make dough. Knead for a few minutes, then place back in the mixing bowl, cover and chill.
3 Meanwhile, fold the filling ingredients together.
4 Roll the dough out to approximately 4mm thick. Use a 12cm (3in) cutter or small bowl to cut out 12 circles. Place a generous tbsp of filling in the centre of each. Brush edges with water and fold to make a half moon parcel. Crimp edges to secure.
5 Brush with beaten egg. Bake for 15-20 minutes until golden brown.
6 Mix all the salsa ingredients and serve alongside.
© www.iguanas.co.uk

3 Monday

4 Tuesday

5 Wednesday

6 Thursday

7 Friday

8 Saturday

9 Sunday

Seems like only yesterday

Grannies came too

Our family holidays were always exciting and very different from the ones our friends had. My father used to hire a car, a Humber, and when it turned up outside our house, we used to squeal with joy. My parents, brother and two sisters would pile in, plus our two grannies, and we would head off on an adventure.

Those were the days before seat belts so, with eight of us squashed in and the roof rack piled high, I had to sit on a stool at my grandmother's feet.

Our journeys were not without problems. I remember, on one occasion, all of us had to get out of the car and walk up an enormous hill, watching anxiously as the Humber slowly reached the top. It wouldn't have made it with our rather large grannies on board! Another time we broke down in Italy and had to rely on the translation skills of a very small boy who somehow sat in the car and guided us to a local garage.

On the way to our destination, we would stop several times and pitch two tents. The smaller one that housed the two grannies used to reverberate at night with the sound of their snoring!

The countries we visited included France, Italy, Portugal and Yugoslavia (as it was known then). I treasure the memories my adventurous parents gave me and they have inspired me to take my own children all over the world, too.

Mrs Sally Petitt, Reading, Berks

It's a fact

The cute little dog who played Toto in The Wizard of Oz was paid more than twice the salary of the human actors who played the Munchkins. Terry, a female Cairns Terrier, got $125 per week, while the short-statured actors playing the Munchkins only got $50 a week.

Turn back time tips

Drink cocoa before bed to help you sleep and boost your brain power. Cocoa is thought to increase blood flow to your brain and is packed with antioxidants for better heart health – go for a good quality one.

Great days out

Bristol Balloon Fiesta

Ashton Court Estate, Bristol
A fantastic opportunity to see balloon flying teams in action. Either turn up early for 'Breakfast and Balloons', to see the first crews of the day rise into the air, or spend an afternoon at the festival in order to catch the evening ascent instead. Better still; stick around for a night show of ballooning and fireworks. The Fiesta usually takes place on the first Thursday-Sunday of August. **Visit www.bristolballoonfiesta. co.uk**

It made me laugh

We were visiting local abbey ruins with my five-year-old grandson, Joe, one summer's day, and saw a bridal party having formal photographs taken. The men were wearing black morning suits, red ties and black top hats. Joe leaned in and whispered: "Are they magicians, Grandma?"
Brenda Clayton, Knaresborough, North Yorkshire

Recipe of the week

Frozen Yogurt Drops

Preparation time: 10 minutes, plus tray freezing
Freezing time: 2 hours

Choose your favourite yogurts to make these delicious yogurt drops:

1 Line a baking tray with clingfilm and place it in the freezer
2 Once the tray is ice–cold, fill a piping bag with your chosen yogurt and pipe small rounds on to the tray
3 Freeze for at least 2 hours until completely hard
4 Remove from the baking tray and serve immediately!
© www.rachelsorganic.co.uk

Mixed Berry Ginger Ice Cream

Serves: 4
Preparation time: 5 minutes

300g (10oz) vanilla flavour yogurt alternative (or yogurt works, too)
300g (10oz) mixed frozen berries
70g (2³/₄oz) stem ginger
1 tbsp honey

Blend all ingredients together and serve in glasses.
© www.alpro.com/uk

10 Monday

11 Tuesday

12 Wednesday

13 Thursday

14 Friday

15 Saturday

16 Sunday

Seems like only yesterday

It was pants!

When I was ten, my dad took us for a holiday in Exmouth where we stayed in a bungalow right by the beach. We met several members of his family there and the photo shows two uncles, three aunts, six cousins, my dad, sister and me outside the bungalow. I'm not sure how we all fitted in but the boys probably slept in a tent in the garden. My sister and I shared a bed with our cousin Joan. We admired her so much as she was slightly older than us, a sophisticated London girl.

When the tide was in we could bathe straight from the fence surrounding the bungalow. The weather that year was glorious. After taking a dip in the sea, one day, I came back to find that my knickers had vanished. This was a source of great embarrassment to me as little girls in those days were brought up to be extremely modest. I approached my auntie and whispered my problem in her ear. To my horror, she stood up and announced to the assembled family: "Dorothy has lost her knickers. Has anybody seen them?"

I nearly died of shame!

To add to my indignity one of our cousins, a teenage boy, quipped: "Well, I haven't got them on!" The whole family roared with laughter.

I can only suppose that the knickers turned up eventually, but I can't remember that part as I was too mortified!

Mrs Dorothy Parry, Southport

It made me laugh

"Doctor, doctor, I keep thinking I'm a goat!"
"How long have you felt like this?"
"Since I was a kid."

June Rogers, Feltham, Middlesex

It's a fact

Winning the National Lottery might be everyone's dream, but it can lead to unwanted drama – one winner broke their leg while dancing in the street outside their house. Some of the most unusual purchases made by National Lottery winners include breast enlargements, a race horse and a castle.

Turn back time tips

You may think that opting for baggy and shapeless clothes are hiding your worst bits, but actually they're more likely to make you look bigger and certainly frumpier. Instead, tailored items and clothing that softly drape your frame will make you look slimmer and enable you to show off your good bits.

Great days out

Holkham Hall

Wells-next-the-Sea, Norfolk
Chamber music, opera and classical music are all performed in Holkham's magnificent Marble Hall throughout the season, and at this time of year the beach and nature reserve are definite must-sees. Make the most of an evening panorama from Gun Hill, after a day of gentle rowing and rambling around the Park, discovering 17th century Ice Houses and the like. **Call 01328 710227 or visit www.holkham.co.uk**

Recipe of the week

Kale, Quinoa and Berry Salad

Serves: 4
Preparation time: 20 minutes
Cooking time: 10–12 minutes

900ml (1¹/₂ pint) vegetable stock
225g (8oz) quinoa
1 tbsp sunflower or rice bran oil
4 tbsp flaked almonds
2 tbsp sunflower seeds
1 tbsp soy sauce
1 tbsp sesame oil
4cm (1¹/₂ inch) piece root ginger, peeled, coarsely grated
2 tsp agave syrup
Freshly ground black pepper
50g (2oz) spinach leaves
50g (2oz) shredded kale
175g (6oz) raspberries
100g (3¹/₂oz) blueberries

1 Add the stock to a saucepan and bring to the boil, add the quinoa and cook for 10–12 minutes or until the grains are beginning to separate. Drain off most of the stock, leaving just enough to keep the grains moist.
2 Meanwhile, heat the oil in a frying pan, add the almonds and sunflower seeds and fry over medium heat until just brown. Take off the heat and stir in the soy sauce. Leave to cool.
3 Add the sesame oil, ginger and agave syrup to the quinoa, season with pepper and transfer to a salad bowl (or plastic container if chilling overnight).
4 Add the spinach and kale leaves, raspberries and blueberries and gently toss together. Sprinkle with the toasted almonds and sunflower seeds to serve.
© www.seasonalberries.co.uk

17 Monday

18 Tuesday

19 Wednesday

20 Thursday

21 Friday

22 Saturday

23 Sunday

Seems like only yesterday

Marvellous Margate

I lived in the Midlands with my parents and younger sister, Valerie, and our favourite seaside resort was Margate, where we stayed at a boarding house in Cliftonville. The total charge for full board for two weeks was under £10.

After a good breakfast, we set off for the beach down a narrow lane and through a tunnel that had been cut out of the cliff. Wooden steps led down to the sand and when the tide was out we played for hours making sandcastles. I remember some bigger children waiting until we had dug a large hole, then they would come over and jump in to smash the sides down. Eventually, we collected some small crabs to greet them next time they attacked us and that put a stop to their game.

We loved to find seaweed and we were told to hang it outside to forecast the weather. If the seaweed was dry, it was going to be fine. We also liked to 'pop' the seaweed to make a satisfying bang.

On the cliff top there was a bandstand and deckchairs where it was nice to sit and listen to the music and sound of the waves. There were clock golf courses and photographers who took photos of children on a stuffed donkey. My father once bought me a Knickerbocker Glory on the condition that I ate the lot. It was a struggle and I had a job to reach the spoon to the bottom of the glass, but I succeeded!

Pat Hawes, Ossett, W Yorkshire

It made me laugh

I was decorating, and was in the middle of scraping my wallpaper off, but had the plumber coming round at the same time. I let him in and left him to his job in the kitchen. As I went back into the lounge to scrape the walls I shouted: "If you need anything I'm just stripping!" Luckily we both saw the funny side.

Mrs M Dinsdale, Newcastle-upon-Tyne

It's a fact

Charlie Chaplin once entered a Charlie Chaplin lookalike contest (which were popular across America when Chaplin first became famous in 1915) in a San Francisco theatre. He lost – not even making it as far as the final round.

Turn back time tips

Our eyes age faster than any other part of our face. Because the skin around the eye area is so delicate, it's more susceptible to damage from the sun – a major cause of ageing. To combat this, wear sunglasses to protect against harmful UV rays and also use an eye cream with a built-in SPF all year round.

Great days out

PIC: CHRIS SCOTT AND EDINBURGH FESTIVAL FRINGE SOCIETY

Fringe Festival

Edinburgh, August
The fringe runs throughout August and showcases the best of UK talent in Scotland's magnificent capital. With thousands of shows on offer, deciding what to see can be a mammoth task. Why not pop into the Half-Price Hut to see what the offers of the day are? Plus there are plenty of free shows – so a little research goes a long way. **Call 0131 226 0026 (tickets can be booked from June on 0131 226 0000) or visit www.edfringe.com/contact-us/box-office**

Recipe of the week

Strawberry Daiquiri Cupcakes

Makes: 12
Preparation time: 20 minutes
Cooking time: 25 minutes

12 large strawberries, chopped
1 tbsp white rum
100g (3^1/$_2$oz) unsalted butter
250g (8oz) caster sugar
50ml (2floz) rapeseed oil
25g (1oz) cornflower
2 tsp vanilla extract
Zest and juice of 1 lime
75ml (3floz) milk
100ml (3^1/$_2$floz) double cream
3 large eggs
300g (10oz) self–raising flour, sifted
Frosting
150g (5oz) strawberries, hulled
1 tbsp lime juice
750ml (1^1/$_4$pt) white rum
175g (6oz) softened unsalted butter
600g (1lb3^1/$_2$oz) icing sugar

1 Preheat oven to 180C/350F/Gas Mark 4, line a muffin tin with cases, and marinade the chopped strawberries in rum.
2 Melt butter over low heat in a small pan. Set aside.
3 Mix sugar, oil, cornflour, vanilla extract and lime zest and juice. Beat in melted butter. Whisk in the egg, followed by milk and cream, then gently fold in flour.
4 Divide strawberries between the cases and spoon mixture over until two–thirds full. Bake for 20-25 minutes until golden and springy. Cool slightly before turning out.
5 For frosting, blend strawberries, lime and rum into purée. Push through a sieve into a bowl.
6 Cream the butter and icing sugar together then gradually add purée. When cool, decorate the cupcakes with frosting, and top with half a strawberry.
© www.mrhughs.co.uk

24 Monday

25 Tuesday

26 Wednesday

27 Thursday

28 Friday

29 Saturday

30 Sunday

Seems like only yesterday

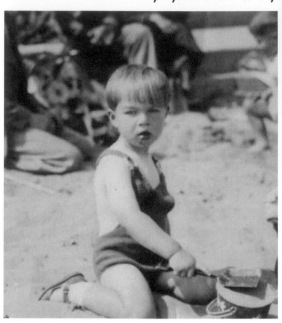

In the swim

I was a dumpy unprepossessing child who watched too much TV. I loved the programme Sea Hunt, set in the Florida Keys and starring the blond hunk Lloyd Bridges. Every week frogman Lloyd, clad in a wetsuit, was attacked by sharks or got trapped in a kelp forest with his oxygen tank running seriously low.

As a result, the local outdoor pool in Boston became my theatre of dreams. It was icy cold and every morning a man in a flat cap skimmed the dead rats off the surface. I was taught to swim there by an immense woman called Mrs Cresswell who operated a gallows-like contraption with which she drew me gently through the water.

Of course, to be like Lloyd I then needed the gear. On a visit to Skegness I had seen a rubber swimming mask with a snorkel and ping-pong ball. I stared long and wistfully at them but the price of 10s 6d was way beyond my pocket, so another fantasy went unfulfilled.

Eventually, Boston swimming baths lost their allure for me. Perhaps, it was the rough kids who stole from the pockets of your clothes left in the disgustingly slimy changing rooms. Or, maybe, it was the swimming galas where the cissy, podgy kids were forced to watch our more athletic companions forging up and down with their heads impressively under water.

However, I do have three swimming certificates that attest to my lengthy devotion to my dream of becoming another Lloyd Bridges.

Alan Whittle, Dorchester, Dorset

It's a fact

The navigationally-challenged little orange fish Nemo from the Disney animation may well be a juvenile male in the film – but he could grow up to be a female! That's because all Clownfish are born male, and it's the largest in the group which becomes female.

Turn back time tips

Eat slowly – it can take up 20 minutes for your stomach to register you're full. Try putting your fork down between mouthfuls. Always have a break before pudding to see if you really need it.

Great days out

PIC. NATIONAL TRUST AND AMHEL DE SERRA

Beatles' Childhood Homes Tour

Woolton and Allerton, Liverpool
As the final week of August is apparently 'International Beatles Week', what better way to celebrate than standing in the spot where John Lennon composed some of his most famous ditties? Visit the childhood homes of bandmates Lennon and McCartney, accompanied by an experienced guide, before you head out into a city filled with Sixties-style celebrations. To book a place on the tour, which lasts approx. 2½ hours. **Call 0151 427 7231 – or visit www.nationaltrust.org.uk/beatles-childhood-homes for more information.**

It made me laugh

Q: How long does it take to make an octopus laugh?
A: Tentickles.

Sarah O'Leary, Bournemouth, Dorset

Recipe of the week

Steak and Noodle Salad with Mango

Serves: 2
Preparation time: 25 minutes
Cooking time: under 20 minutes

200g (7oz) thin cut or flash fry steaks
150g (5oz) wholewheat noodles
4 tsp rapeseed or olive oil
1 small red onion, finely sliced
1 large carrot, peeled and cut into strips
1 small red pepper, deseeded and cut into strips
100g (3½oz) freshly chopped kale
1 small mango, peeled, and cut into strips
Grated zest and juice of 1 lime
Salt and pepper

1 Cook the noodles according to packet instructions, drain, rinse and set aside.
2 Heat a large frying pan or wok and heat 1 tbsp oil. Add the onion, carrot and pepper. Cook for 1–2 minutes, stirring occasionally. Add the kale or chard and cook for 2–3 minutes. Stir through the noodles.
3 Meanwhile, preheat the grill to moderate.
4 Add the mango, lime zest and half the juice to the pan. Toss gently. Season and set aside.
5 Season and rub the steaks with the remaining oil on both sides. Grill for 1–2 minutes on each side. Leave to rest on a warm plate, then cut into slices and toss into the noodle salad.
6 Spoon on to a warm plate, drizzle with remaining lime juice and serve.
© www.simplybeefandlamb.co.uk

31 Monday

1 Tuesday

2 Wednesday

3 Thursday

4 Friday

5 Saturday

6 Sunday

Seems like only yesterday

Tiptoe to the toilet

Until I was 12 I lived in Regent Street – no, not the one in London, this one was in Derby, near the railway station. When I was 11 I found out from a school friend that I lived in the 'slums'. That came as a bit of a shock to me as there was nothing slummish about our house.

However, it was true that there was no bathroom. The toilet stood at the end of the garden. Going there could be something of an adventure, particularly on dark winter evenings. My sister accompanied me when I was little, but as I grew bigger and braver I learned to take the torch and shine it all around the whitewashed walls so that I knew the whereabouts of every daddy longlegs in the tiny room. Then there were moths to watch out for as well!

If you remember Izal toilet paper, you will know that it was a bit uncomfortable compared with today's soft tissue. But my grandfather (who was made of stern stuff) had his own brand of toilet paper which was made up of the pages of the Radio Times cut into quarters with a penknife and hung together on a piece of string.

In the photo, our lavatory door can be seen behind my sister Joan who is on the right and my cousin Kevin is on the left. That's me in the middle with Jimmy the kitten on my lap.

Doris Brown, Derby

It made me laugh

My son cut the front of his hair with some baby nail scissors, two weeks before he was due to start school for the first time. "What have you done?!" I asked, horrified. He smiled widely and said: "I wanted to look like Daddy." Unfortunately, my husband had a rapidly receding hairline!

Mrs M Saunders, Barkingside, London

It's a fact

In the English language, 'forty' is the only number that has all of its letters in alphabetical order, while 'four' is the only one which is spelt with the same number of letters as the number itself.

Turn back time tips

Our lips thin as we age, so need help to make them look younger and fuller. Always use a lip liner to give them shape and to prevent lipstick seeping into fine lines. Stick to a neutral lip liner and opt for plumping hydrating lip colours. For added pout apply a little highlighter above your cupid's bow.

Great days out

Burghley Horse Trials

Burghley House, Stamford, Lincolnshire, Sep 3-6
Burghley is a truly beautiful destination all year round, with its Gardens of Surprise and the House itself (a stunning example of Elizabethan architecture). However, most exciting are the Horse Trials, held here every September. Whether you can make the Trials or not, be sure to take an autumn stroll around the grounds, through the avenues of trees to see the local deer. **Call 01780 752451 or visit www.burghley.co.uk**

Recipe of the week

Chunky Vegetable and Black Bean Stew

Serves: 6
Preparation time: 15-20 minutes
Cooking time: 35 minutes

2 tbsp olive oil
2 onions, chopped
4 garlic cloves, crushed
2 red chillies, deseeded and finely chopped
1 heaped tsp ground cumin
400g can chopped tomatoes
600ml (1pt) hot vegetable stock
6 tbsp cranberry sauce
450g (1lb) butternut squash, peeled and cut into chunks
1 cinnamon stick
150g (5oz) baby corn
150g (5oz) sugar snap peas
250g (8oz) cherry tomatoes
400g can black beans, rinsed and drained
Salt and pepper
1 tbsp cornflour
4 tbsp crème fraîche
2 tbsp dried cranberries, chopped
Small handful mint and coriander leaves, chopped

1 Fry the onion in the oil for 4-5 minutes until softened and beginning to colour. Stir in the garlic, chillies and cumin and stir for 1 minute. Add tomatoes, stock, cranberry sauce, butternut squash and the cinnamon stick, then bring to the boil. Cover and simmer for 10 minutes.
2 Stir in the baby corn, sugar snap peas, cherry tomatoes and beans. Simmer uncovered for 8-10 minutes until the squash is tender but holds its shape.
3 Mix cornflour with 2 tbsp cold water until smooth. Stir into the stew for 1-2 minutes, until thickened. Season to taste and serve with crème fraîche, scattered with dried cranberries and herbs.
© www.oceanspray.co.uk

7	Monday

8	Tuesday

9	Wednesday

10	Thursday

11	Friday

12	Saturday

13	Sunday

Seems like only yesterday

Anne, aged 17

As easy as ABC?

The first day at school was a scary experience for a five year old. In those days there were no nurseries or introduction days so we were plunged straight into this bewildering world. Fortunately, I had a twin sister so I wasn't alone. We set off together in neatly pressed gymslips and smart blazers, our shoes highly polished, carrying our brand-new leather schoolbags.

The school was a very old building with high windows so it was impossible for the pupils to see the world outside. Iron railings enclosed the school and as we peered through them we wondered if we would ever get out again.

The infant teacher was kind and pleasant, but discipline was fairly strict. The desks were set out in rows. You sat in your place and didn't move. We learned by rote, reading from a beginner's reader, chanting tables. All eyes were on the huge clock that hung behind the teacher's desk. How slowly the minutes ticked away! And how thankfully we joined in the hymn that we sang at the end of every day.

Outside school we did other things like collecting sheep's wool and sphagnum moss to be made into dressings (this was during the war). Later, we learned to knit and my sister, more skilled than I was, knitted a pair of socks for a relative in the RAF. My khaki scarf was full of dropped stitches – pity the unfortunate soldier who received it!

Anne Forsyth, St Andrews, Fife

It's a fact

The puma is a big cat with an identity crisis – it holds the record for having more recorded names than any other mammal, with more than 40 names in English alone. These include: puma, cougar, panther, mountain lion, mountain cat, painter, and the descriptive 'mountain screamer'.

Turn back time tips

Book an eye test: 50 per cent of people over 40 haven't had a test for five years, putting their sight at risk. Regular tests mean that age-related sight problems such as AMD and cataracts can be picked up quickly.

Great days out

Leeds Castle Food Festival

Broomfield, Kent, Sep 11-13
Food fans will love this annual event, just in its second year, which takes place in the spectacular backdrop of Leeds Castle. The building itself has a reading room to rival the library from Beauty and the Beast (well, almost) and you can even book an 'Owl Experience'… Can't make this weekend? Head along from Sep 22-27 for the Festival of Flowers instead.
Call 01622 765400 or visit www.leeds-castle.com

It made me laugh

"Doctor, doctor, I can't stop singing 'The Green, Green Grass of Home'!"
"That sounds like Tom Jones syndrome."
"Is it common?"
"It's not unusual."

Ruth Kingston, via email

Recipe of the week

Spaghetti with Leeks, Peas, Bacon and Lemon

Serves: 4
Preparation time: 15 minutes
Cooking time: 15 minutes

400g (13oz) dried spaghetti
40g (1^1/$_2$oz) butter
150g (5oz) bacon lardons
200g (7oz) leeks, finely chopped
400ml (14floz) crème fraîche
100g (3^1/$_2$oz) cooked peas
Juice and zest of 1 lemon
Salt and pepper
Small bunch flat leaf parsley, chopped
50g (2oz) Parmesan, grated

1 Bring a medium pan of salted water to the boil, add spaghetti and cook according to the packet instructions
2 Meanwhile, fry the bacon over a low heat until the fat releases. Turn up the heat so it starts to colour, (after about 5 minutes), then add the leeks and cook for another 5 minutes.
3 Add the crème fraîche and cook until it starts to bubble and reduce. By now your pasta should be cooked. Drain and set aside.
4 Add the lemon juice and zest to your sauce, season to taste and add the chopped parsley.
5 Toss the pasta in sauce and serve, sprinkled with Parmesan.
© www.britishleeks.co.uk

September 14 - 20

14 Monday

15 Tuesday

16 Wednesday

17 Thursday

18 Friday

19 Saturday

20 Sunday

Seems like only yesterday

Fields of gold

My late Dad's photo album is full of memories of my time growing up in Lincolnshire. He filed all the pictures meticulously in date order, each with its own caption. He called this one Buttercups and Daisies and it shows me with my sister Joy in 1961 when I was five and she was nine.

We were on one of our favourite walks down by the River Trent. Dad would take us out every Sunday morning when he taught us all we knew about nature; spotting frogs in ditches, identifying wild flowers and birds, the tracks of different animals.

We loved this field which was a carpet of buttercups and daisies from late spring to the end of summer. There were no restrictions on picking wild flowers then so we would spend happy times shining buttercups under each other's chins 'to see if we liked butter' as well as making daisy-chain headbands, necklaces and bracelets for ourselves. We felt like princesses in all our finery. We took some home with us to adorn our Mum.

Maybe, it's partly as a result of our enthusiastic jewellery making that you don't see many buttercup meadows nowadays. There were many more of them then and I am only sorry that I won't be able to take my beautiful granddaughter, Eva, on that same walk we shared with Dad. Those shining fields of white and gold could you cheer you up even on the gloomiest day.

Mrs Claire Waite, Retford, Notts

It made me laugh

Q: Why are there no aspirin in the jungle?
A: Because the parrots eat 'em all.

June Smith, Enfield, London

It's a fact

The US police force is kept busy, with a whopping 2.2 million residents kept behind bars – more than anywhere else. The nation has just five per cent of the world's population, yet holds a quarter of the global incarcerated population. China is in second place at 1.5 million and Russia comes third at 870,000.

Turn back time tips

We all eat too much salt. Have two pinches less salt a day to help reduce your risk of heart disease. Use herbs and spices to give your food flavour instead.

Great days out

Kent Life

Heritage Park, Sandling, Kent

Step back in time and discover what life was once like in the Garden of England. The vintage village is a wonderful collection of buildings saved from demolition and carefully re-assembled – with each house decorated to represent different eras, from Victorian to the Fifties. With the gardens, orchard and Dotty's Fifties Tearoom, there's plenty to keep you occupied. **Call 01622 763936 or visit www.kentlife.org.uk**

Recipe of the week

Plum Crumble

Serves: 4
Preparation time: 20 minutes
Cooking time: 25 minutes

750g (1½lb) plums, washed, stoned and halved
150g (5oz) demerara sugar
Juice and zest of 1 orange
150g (5oz) plain flour
60g (2¼oz) butter
25g (1oz) flaked almonds
50g (2oz) rolled oats

1 Preheat the oven to 180°C/350°F/Gas Mark 4. Place the plum halves in a pan with half the sugar, orange juice and zest. Cook gently for 10 minutes to soften.
2 Meanwhile, place the flour into a bowl and rub in the butter with your fingertips, until the mixture resembles fine breadcrumbs. Stir in the remaining sugar, flaked almonds and oats.
3 Divide the fruit between 4 ovenproof dishes and spoon over crumble mixture.
4 Bake for 20–25 minutes until golden and bubbling.
© www.budgens.co.uk

21 Monday

22 Tuesday

23 Wednesday

24 Thursday

25 Friday

26 Saturday

27 Sunday

Seems like only yesterday

Playing footsie

Days out were rare when I was a child as my parents never owned a car and could not afford to take the whole family away for a holiday, so it was a great treat when the school took us on a day trip to Whipsnade Zoo.

This photo (taken by one our teachers) is of me with my first love, Mark Thorpe, who as you can see was a few inches shorter then I was but that didn't matter to us. We were both ten years old and he was in the same class as me in junior school. He would buy me a cup of squash and a biscuit at break-time and after school I used to play football with him in the park. Unusually, for those days, there were a few girls who joined in the games of football, although some of the boys didn't like us taking part.

Mark and I didn't sit next to each other on the coach that took us to Whipsnade as he was quite shy and my best friend might have been jealous (and as I used to be extremely travel sick, he probably made the right decision).

His rather formal pink floral shirt with button-down collar and contrasting paisley tie are a far cry from the trainers and hoodies that boys might wear for a school trip today, but they were very trendy back in 1972! **Mrs Kate Hardy, Kettering**

It made me laugh

I was walking back from the shops just as the light was starting to fade. In front of me in the middle of the path was a hedgehog, so I bent over to have a look saying: "Aren't you sweet?" But, on closer inspection, it turned out to be a baseball hat that had been dropped – the peak was what I thought was the hedgehog's snout!"
Lynn O'Shea, Wellingborough, Northamptonshire

It's a fact

Your skin accounts for around 15 per cent of your body weight, and the average skin, when stretched, would cover two square metres. Horrifyingly you shed 30,000 dead skin cells every minute – that explains the amount of dusting we have to do.

Turn back time tips

While comforting, head to toe black is ageing and can make pale skin tones look washed out. Try navy as an alternative – it's chic, still has the slimming benefits and is softer so suits most skin tones. If you can't face turning your back on black, add colourful accessories – a scarf or statement necklace – to instantly liven up your look.

Great days out

Stitch, Sew & Hobbycrafts

Westpoint, Exeter, Sep 24-27
Whether you're looking for inspiration, or simply need to get your hands on those elusive supplies, get involved with this collection of workshops, talks and demonstrations on all things crafty. There is usually a must-see exhibition or two as well – last year the costumes from the film adaptation of Les Misérables were on display, as well as a collection of vintage handbags, hats and gloves from 1890 to 1960! Sounds right up our street. **Call 01425 272711 for general enquiries and 01425 277988 for tickets. Visit www.ichfevents.co.uk**

Recipe of the week

Lentil and cashew nut roast

Makes: 1 loaf
Preparation time: 30 minutes
Cooking time: 1 hour

75g (3oz) pimiento piquillo peppers, finely chopped
200g (7oz) red split lentils
450ml (³/₄pt) vegetable stock
1 bay leaf
100g (3¹/₂oz) unsalted cashew nuts
1¹/₂ tbsp olive oil
1 large onion, finely chopped
1 large leek, finely chopped
100g (3¹/₂oz) mushrooms, finely chopped
1 garlic clove, crushed
1 tbsp lemon juice
100g (3¹/₂oz) wholemeal breadcrumbs
3 tbsp chopped parsley
75g (3oz) mature cheddar, grated
1 egg, lightly beaten

1 Rinse and drain lentils. Bring them to the boil with stock and bay leaf.
2 Reduce heat to a simmer and cover for 15 minutes, stirring occasionally, to absorb stock. Discard bay leaf.
3 Meanwhile: toast cashews over moderate heat until lightly browned, then chop. Preheat oven to 190°C/375°F/Gas Mark 5. Line a 1.4kg (2³/₄lb) loaf tin.
4 Fry the onion in oil, over moderate heat, for 5 minutes. Add vegetables and garlic for another 5, stirring occasionally. Add lemon juice.
5 Tip mixture into a bowl. Stir in breadcrumbs, nuts, parsley, cheese and egg. Season, then spoon into tin. Cover with lightly-oiled foil.
6 Bake for 30 minutes, remove foil, then bake for another 30, until a skewer comes out clean. Turn out after 10 minutes, and slice.
© www.fragata.co.uk

28 Monday

29 Tuesday

30 Wednesday

1 Thursday

2 Friday

3 Saturday

4 Sunday

Seems like only yesterday

Home from home

This is a recent photo of the house where my sister Lily and I were evacuated during the war. It was owned by Mr and Mrs Guile who looked after us for four years. I must have been happy because I have no bad memories. Mrs Guile was a good cook who made several types of jam in the fruit season. Mr Guile used to shoot wild rabbits and we had delicious rabbit stew. I loved wash-day on Mondays. A mangle was kept in an outhouse by the kitchen and we helped by turning the handle.

We walked to the village school carrying our gas masks in a cardboard box. Miss Foster was the only teacher and lived in a house next door to the school. Some of the local boys were quite a handful. They stood on their desks and taunted Miss Foster. They didn't like evacuees and used to say: "Go back to London!"

When we were older we cycled to school in Thakeham. It was a lovely school with a gymnasium, a cookery room for domestic science and a laboratory. In the winter we couldn't go to school when the snow was so deep it came up past the tops of our Wellingtons. Mr Guile made a sledge and used to run us up and down the road on it.

In the summer, Mum and Dad and my uncle came to visit us. A friend of Dad's who had a taxi used to bring them down.

Mrs Rosina Coomber, Sutton, Surrey

It made me laugh

My daughter and I were out for the day, and decided to stop off for a meal at a nearby pub. On the menu was the 'Lion Burger'. Horrified, my vegetarian daughter said: "I never knew they made those!" When we were on our way out I happened to look up and saw the name of the pub – The White Lion. It explained a lot!

Mrs Clarke, via email

It's a fact

The smallest living dog, in terms of height, is a female Chihuahua called Miracle Milly, who measured 9.65 cm (3.8 in) tall on February 21, 2013 and is owned by Vanesa Semler of Dorado, Puerto Rico.

Turn back time tips

The skin on our hands is quite thin and they're constantly exposed to the elements, which is why they show ageing signs quicker than anywhere else. Look after them with a hand cream with built-in SPF and by wearing gloves outside whenever it's cold and also when washing up. For a youth boost, use your anti-ageing serum on the backs of your hands too.

Great days out

Isle of Anglesey

North Wales

You might be familiar with the name of this island, but have you actually visited? Wrap up warm for a guided tour on the water around the Menai S traits **(Call 0333 123 4303 or visit www.ribride.co.uk)**, or head to the Farmer's Market on the third Saturday of the month for freshly baked bread, organic mushrooms and locally caught crab. This 220 square miles of unspoilt coast and landscape is designated an Area of Outstanding National Beauty – including Roman remains, no less!

Recipe of the week

Spicy Butternut Squash Soup

Serves: 2-3
Preparation time: 15 minutes
Cooking time: 30 minutes

1 medium butternut squash, peeled and chopped
2 tbsp olive oil
1 chilli, chopped and deseeded
2 potatoes, peeled and cubed
1 onion, chopped
1l (1³/₄pt) vegetable stock
Salt and pepper

1 Chop the squash, onion and potatoes into cubes. Oil a warm pot and cook onions and chilli until soft. Then add potatoes and squash.
2 After a minute or so, add vegetable stock and simmer for about 30 minutes or until potatoes and squash are soft. Using a blender or food processor, blend the soup until smooth. If too thick, add a little water.
3 Season to taste and serve with thick, crusty bread.
© www.livlivefoods.co.uk

5	Monday

6	Tuesday

7	Wednesday

8	Thursday

9	Friday

10	Saturday

11	Sunday

Seems like only yesterday

Happy together

My grandparents had this photo of me taken to send to my mother who was in a sanatorium with TB. The adoring expression on my face is for my Dadcu (Welsh for grandfather) who was the centre of my universe. Unlike my grandmother whose attitude to children was somewhat stern and Victorian, he was a gentle soul who patiently tolerated being followed around from dawn to dusk by a devoted little chatterbox.

Our daily routine mostly involved constructive pottering. There were chickens to feed and tomatoes to be watered in the greenhouse. If it was raining, we retreated to Dadcu's shed which smelt pleasantly of fresh wood shavings. On Friday evenings, we sat together at the cloth-covered table in the front room to count the takings of the village shop run by my grandmother. Threepenny bits were sorted into piles of four, pennies into piles of twelve and so on.

Unless he was going to church or into town, Dadcu was usually dressed in work trousers and waistcoat, shirt sleeves rolled up, with a flat tweed cap on his head. His waistcoat pockets held a watch on a chain as well as Victory-V sweets. These were so strongly flavoured that I was only allowed to have half of one as a treat.

When we were not pottering, we liked to read. While Dadcu enjoyed a crime thriller by Edgar Wallace, I devoured the latest Enid Blyton adventure – and was silent for a change!

Mary Anne Price, Downham Market, Norfolk

It's a fact

Fancy a bit of peace and quiet? Head for the Falkland Islands, where the only noise is gentle bleating – because there are 350 sheep for every person. With only about 3,000 residents the Islands are home to approximately 500,000 sheep. Not surprisingly wool is a major export.

Turn back time tips

It may be tempting to always reach for those sensible, sturdy and comfy shoes, but clumpy and boring footwear can ruin even the most gorgeous outfit. Nowadays, there are lots of brands that have created comfortable, yet stylish flats and heels, so there's absolutely no excuse for letting your footwear bring you down!

Great days out

Woburn Abbey

Woburn Park, Bedfordshire
Home to the Duke and Duchess of Bedford, you might be more familiar with Woburn for its zoo. However, the Abbey and deer park are also worth a peek, particularly in autumn, when the colours are at their most vibrant. There are nine different species of deer found across the 3,000 acres – which make it one of the largest private conservation parks in Europe. **Call 01525 290333 or visit www.woburnabbey.co.uk**

It made me laugh

Q: What's the difference between a cat and a comma?
A: One has claws at the end of its paws and the other has a pause at the end of its clause.
William Maynard, Tonbridge, Kent

Recipe of the week

Creamy Fish Pie

Serves: 4
Preparation time: 25 minutes
Cooking time: 1hour 15 minutes

2 tbsp sunflower oil
1 large onion, finely chopped
110g (4oz) carrots, peeled and chopped
100g (3½oz) watercress, chopped
500g (1lb) celeriac, peeled and cubed
850g (1¾lb) potatoes, peeled and quartered
25g (1oz) butter
150ml (¼pt) semi-skimmed milk
400g (13oz) cod fillet, skinned and cut into pieces
350g (12oz) smoked haddock fillet, skinned and cut into pieces
2 hard-boiled eggs, peeled and quartered
350ml (12floz) double cream
Salt and ground black pepper

1 Heat the oil in a large pan and cook the onion and carrot for 10-15 minutes until softened. Cook the watercress for 1 minute to wilt. Leave to cool.
2 Place the celeriac and potatoes in a pan of salted water. Bring to the boil and simmer until soft (about 15 minutes). Drain well, then mash with butter and milk. Season to taste.
3 Arrange the fish in a shallow pie dish, with egg quarters on top. Spoon over the carrot, onion and watercress. Season before pouring over the cream.
4 Spoon over the mashed potatoes and celeriac. Cook in a pre-heated oven at 200°C/400°F/Gas Mark 6 for 45 minutes, until golden brown and bubbling.
© www.watercress.co.uk

12 Monday	
13 Tuesday	
14 Wednesday	
15 Thursday	
16 Friday	
17 Saturday	
18 Sunday	

Seems like only yesterday

Beret bad girl

This photo takes me back to a carefree summer in the early Sixties when I played Rosaline in the school's production of Love's Labours Lost. That's me standing next to the Princess of Aquitaine in the school garden which was the perfect setting for a Shakespeare comedy.

To my mother's dismay, the costume I'm wearing was green – a colour she believed to be unlucky, but despite that bad omen all went well. It didn't rain, I remembered my lines and we got a kind review in the local paper.

Tewkesbury High School for Girls was a world away from today's academies. Small enough to occupy an elegant Victorian town house, it was staffed by spinsters of a certain age, several of whom had lost their fiancés in the First World War. They wore sensible tweed skirts, thick lisle stockings and stout lace-up shoes. Much to our delight, the geography teacher, Miss Baker, favoured knee-length pink bloomers into which she discreetly tucked her handkerchief.

I didn't expect to be chosen to play Rosaline as I wasn't a great favourite of the headmistress (Miss Craighead – known to us as Craggers, of course) being guilty of misdemeanours such as wearing my school beret at a jaunty non-regulation angle, sneaking out to the café across the road instead of playing hockey, and working as a waitress at weekends when I should have been studying for 'A' levels. Tut tut! But at least I never joined the rebels who smoked behind the bike shed.

Marion Reeve, Swaffham, Norfolk

It made me laugh

A man went into a shop and asked a sales assistant, "Do you sell potato clocks?"
"Potato clocks?" replied the assistant. "I'm not sure what you mean."
"It's my boss," the man explained. "I'm always late for work at nine o'clock, but he keeps telling me there wouldn't be a problem if I got a potato clock."

Marilyn Saunders, Truro, Cornwall

It's a fact

People tell more lies in January than any other month. The average person tells 217 lies in January (about seven per day). Usually about what they did over the Christmas holidays, what presents they received or gave, just how much they gorged themselves on holiday food, and, perhaps, how happy they are to see all their co-workers again!

Turn back time tips

Snack on carrot sticks as they're packed with Vitamin A, which is great for your eyes and they also fill you up for just a few calories. Keep a stash in the fridge for when you feel peckish.

Great days out

Coalport China Museum

Nr. Ironbridge, Shropshire
Alongside the River Severn, on the site of the original Coalport China Works, is this intriguing tribute to china. Watch how fine china was made and then fired, in earthenware containers called saggars. The reconstructed kiln, or updraught bottle oven, kicks out a fair bit of heat and you can also find out how the workers managed day-to-day in the factory. **Call 01952 433424 or visit www.ironbridge.org.uk**

Recipe of the week

Lamb Cawl

Serves: 4
Preparation time: 30 minutes
Cooking time: 90 minutes

450g (1lb) lean lamb shoulder, cubed
1 tbsp oil
1 onion, cut into wedges
450ml (³/₄pt) lamb stock
1 leek, sliced
2 carrots, peeled and sliced
Sprig fresh thyme and rosemary
3 large potatoes, peeled and cubed
75g (3oz) frozen peas
2 large handfuls curly kale
Dumplings:
100g (3¹/₂oz) self-raising flour
50g (2oz) suet
2 tbsp fresh rosemary, chopped
Water

1 Pre-heat oven to 180°C/350°F/Gas Mark 4.
2 Heat the oil in a large ovenproof pan and lightly brown the lamb and onion. Add all remaining ingredients except peas and curly kale, and bring to the boil. Cover and cook for 1–1¹/₂ hours.
3 Meanwhile, for the dumplings, mix flour and suet and stir in rosemary. Bind with a little water. Divide into small balls then drop into the broth. Cover and cook for 20 minutes until dumplings are fluffy and risen. Remove dumplings once cooked and keep warm.
4 Add remaining vegetables roughly 10 minutes before end of cooking and heat through. Ladle into bowls, add dumplings, sprinkle with chives and serve.
© www.eatwelshlamb.co.uk

19 Monday

20 Tuesday

21 Wednesday

22 Thursday

23 Friday

24 Saturday

25 Sunday

Seems like only yesterday

Mine's a pint!

In 1964 when I was aged five, my younger sister Kate and I were asked to be flower girls at the wedding of some friends of my parents who didn't have any young relatives they could ask. Mum was absolutely delighted and thrilled to bits with our pretty dresses (salmon pink with matching ribbons in our hair). Dad wore his best suit for the occasion and I remember Mum looked very trim in her matching two-piece.

It was a perfect warm summer's day and, as we followed her and the bridesmaids up the aisle, we thought the bride looked like a princess in her long traditional white dress. Naturally, we were very excited by the whole experience, but were warned that we had to behave ourselves and not spoil the bride's big day – or there would be trouble!

All went well and we behaved impeccably until, at the reception party afterwards, my little sister accidentally drank a glass full of beer that had been left on the table by another guest. Inebriated at the tender age of two! You can see in the photo her damp fringe and slightly flushed expression as the drink took effect. Apparently, she slept very well that night!

As it happened, we were never asked to be bridesmaids or flower girls again (maybe because Kate got 'drunk') so we always remember that day with special affection.

Elaine Mackie, Kettering, Northants

It made me laugh

Q: When is a door not a door?
A: When it's ajar.

Kate Hardy, Kettering, Northamptonshire

It's a fact

We've all heard the advice about walking 10,000 steps per day for good health, but in fact the average person walks the equivalent of three times around the world in a lifetime. 9.1 million adults in England, or 22 per cent of the population, walk recreationally for at least 30 minutes in four weeks.

Turn back time tips

If your eyelashes are a bit sparse don't skip eyeliner, but do avoid pen or gel eyeliners that give an unnatural thick line making your eyes look smaller. Instead, try blending a grey or taupe eyeshadow into your upper lash line using a fine brush or cotton bud. This will shape your eyes and give definition to droopy eyelids.

Great days out

Crafts for Christmas

SECC Hall 5, Glasgow, Oct 22-25
Can't believe it's that time of year again? Neither can we! But if, like Scouts you believe in being prepared – go along to the Crafts for Christmas show. As well as crafty exhibitions there's a place for festive food and drink, plus live music and a gift-wrapping service. Buy a readymade wonder, or find the elements to make your very own presents from scratch. **Call 01425 272711 for general enquiries and 01425 277988 for tickets. Visit www.ichfevents.co.uk**

Recipe of the week

Apple Sage Tarte Tatin

Serves: 8
Preparation time: 20 minutes
Cooking time: 50 minutes

275ml (9floz) cider
125g (4oz) sugar
175g (6oz) butter, cubed
4 tsp molasses
4 apples, peeled and halved
$1^1/_2$ tsp chopped sage
1 sheet puff pastry
125ml (4floz) sunflower oil for frying (optional)
Fresh sage leaves (optional)

1 Preheat oven to 200°C/400°F/Gas Mark 6.
2 Bring cider to the boil in a 25cm (10in) heavy-based, ovenproof pan. Cook over medium heat for 10 minutes until reduced by half. Reduce heat to medium, stir in sugar and cook for 5 minutes until caramel begins to brown. Stir in butter and molasses.
3 Place apples cut sides up in the caramel, packing tightly. Cook for 3-5 minutes. Remove from heat, sprinkle with chopped sage, then place pastry on top, tucking sides in.
4 Bake for 20-25 minutes until golden, then cool on a wire rack for 5 minutes.
5 Meanwhile, heat oil in a small pan over medium-high heat. Fry 4-6 sage leaves at a time for 3 seconds, until crisp. Drain on paper towels.
6 Run a small knife around the inside edge of pan, then flip on to a serving platter so the pastry makes a crust. Allow to cool and garnish with sage.
© www.schwartz.co.uk/recipes

26 Monday

27 Tuesday

28 Wednesday

29 Thursday

30 Friday

31 Saturday

1 Sunday

Seems like only yesterday

Radio times

Our village, Longbridge Hayes, consisted of four streets of terraced houses set in a square, and boasted two churches and two corner shops. I have happy memories of a time when doors could be left open without fear of burglars.

Dad worked in Silverdale pit, so we were fortunate in having plenty of coal available and there was always a good fire burning in our grate. It was my job to blacklead the grate every week and to polish the brass fender surround.

We didn't have electricity until I was 11, but we had a gas meter into which my mum put her pennies. We had a radio and on Sundays my brother and I had to take the accumulator into nearby Longport to be exchanged for a refill. As it was heavy this was quite a considerable task, but we didn't mind because we didn't want to miss programmes such as Dick Barton, Two-Way Family Favourites or The Man in Black with Valentine Dyall.

Summers were spent outdoors in Bradwell Woods where we built dens or tied ropes to the trees to play Tarzan. In the holidays, our parents were quite happy for us to take jam sandwiches and bottles of water and wander off for the day. We played hopscotch in the streets or swung around the lampposts until we were called for bed.

I lived in the village until I was 18 years old but, unfortunately, it no longer exists as it was bulldozed to make way for an industrial estate.

Freda Lowe, Newcastle-under-Lyme

It made me laugh

Q: Why do demons and ghouls get along so well?
A: Because demons are a ghoul's best friend.

Rebecca Taylor, Reading, Berkshire

It's a fact

There are more living organisms in a teaspoonful of soil than there are people alive on Earth, with one individual gram of healthy soil capable of containing several billion bacteria from thousands of different species. On top of which, scientists estimate that for every human, there are 200 million insects on earth.

Turn back time tips

If your legs are no longer your best bit, you may consider hiding them under baggy trousers and floor-length skirts is the only option. In fact a skirt that sits just below the knee is a flattering and youthful option that will show off the slimmest parts of your legs while hiding problem areas like the thighs and knees.

Great days out

Lord Stones Country Park

Chop Gate, North Yorkshire
This 160-acre park is named after the standing stones at its Bronze Age burial site, which marks the centre of the Cleveland Way, the Lyke Wake Walk and the coast-to-coast path. Historians will also love finding out about the Second World War decoys and the collection of local, 5,000-year-old flint arrowheads in the restaurant. Enjoying yourself too much? Stay the night in a luxury camping pod! **Call 01642 778482 or visit www.lordstones.com**

Recipe of the week

Stuffed Pumpkins

Serves: 4
Preparation time: 25 minutes
Cooking time: 1 hour

2 x 700–800g (1¹/₂lb) pumpkins, halved and pips scooped out
75g (3oz) couscous
2 tbsp olive oil
1 leek, washed, trimmed and sliced
175g (6oz) chestnut mushrooms, chopped
50g (2oz) pine nuts
2 tbsp parsley, chopped
100g (3¹/₂oz) feta cheese, crumbled
Freshly milled black pepper

1 Preheat the oven to 190°C/375°F/Gas Mark 5. Place the pumpkin halves on a baking tray and cook for 40 minutes.
2 Meanwhile, pour 100ml (3¹/₂floz) cold water over the couscous and leave to stand for 10 minutes.
3 Heat 1 tbsp olive oil in a pan and cook leeks for 3-4 minutes before adding mushrooms. Cook for a further 5-6 minutes, until all are softened.
4 Fluff up the couscous with a fork then stir into the leek and mushroom mixture, along with the pine nuts, parsley and feta. Season with pepper.
5 Spoon the stuffing mixture into the pumpkin halves, drizzle with the remaining olive oil and bake for a further 15 minutes.
© www.budgens.co.uk

2	Monday
3	Tuesday
4	Wednesday
5	Thursday
6	Friday
7	Saturday
8	Sunday

Seems like only yesterday

I had a little lamb

I wish the children of today could enjoy the freedom I had as a child growing up in the Sixties, even though times were hard. We lived in a small house on a farm owned by our neighbours. My brother and I would spend all day playing on the farm or in the woods, making dens. I was a real tomboy and would often be found at the top of the highest tree.

I loved being in the milking parlour when the cows were being milked and feeding them cow cake. Of course, a handful of cow cake would sometimes accidentally find its way into my mouth too!

I adored cats and there were many of them around the place, but I was only allowed to have one as an indoor pet. Its name was Smokey. My brother had a pet pig which, if I remember correctly, was called Percy. It used to follow us around the yard, snuffling and grunting.

One day a lamb came down the lane and began following me around the garden. Wherever I went, it was right behind me – it even followed me into the house. As you can imagine, my mum was not happy about the lamb droppings everywhere!

The lamb, named Molly, became my pet and – like the nursery rhyme – wherever I went, the lamb was sure to go. Often I would sit by the window crying as Molly looked in, wanting to come into the house to be with me.

Mrs Elizabeth Richards, Haverfordwest, Pembs

It's a fact

It's surprising how much of life is a matter of timing – even your height changes depending on the clock, with most people finding themselves 1 per cent shorter in the evening than they were first thing. Weather-wise, it is most likely to be raining at 7am and least likely at 3am.

Turn back time tips

Keep your feet supple and boost circulation by lifting your heels up and down off the floor, wiggling your toes and circling your heels. Do it a few times a day and it could help to reduce puffy ankles too.

Great days out

National Railway Museum

York

Explore giant halls full of railway legends such as the Mallard, and soak up the atmosphere in Station Hall, before watching engineers at work. Travel back in time to experience working life in a station, then take a peek at the opulent carriages of Queen Victoria and the armour-plated war transport of George VI. There's always an exhibition on in the gallery and lots to keep you occupied on a wet afternoon.
Call 0844 815 3139 or visit www.nrm.org.uk

It made me laugh

Q: What do you get if you cross a dog and a telephone?
A: A golden receiver.

Sharon Norman, Fleetwood, Lancashire

Recipe of the week

Banana and Chocolate Yogurt Muffins

Makes: 6
Preparation time: 10 minutes
Cooking time: 25–30 minutes

130g (4^{1}/$_{4}$oz) plain flour
130g (4^{1}/$_{4}$oz) plain wholemeal flour
1 1/2 tsp baking powder
250g (8oz) vanilla yogurt, or yogurt alternative
40g (1^{3}/$_{4}$oz) dark chocolate, chopped into chunks
2 bananas, mashed
100ml (3^{1}/$_{2}$floz) agave syrup
150ml (^{1}/$_{4}$pt) rapeseed oil
1 egg

1 Preheat oven to 180°C/350°F/Gas Mark 4. Put the plain and wholemeal flours, chocolate chunks and baking powder into a large bowl.
2 Add the yogurt/yogurt alternative, rapeseed oil, banana, agave syrup and egg to a separate bowl, and whisk together until smooth. Fold the dry mixture into the wet mixture using a metal spoon.
3 Line a 6-hole muffin tray with muffin cases. Fill each case two-thirds full and bake for 25–30 minutes.
Top tip: Decorate your muffins with a few extra slices of banana!
© www.alpro.com/uk

9	Monday
10	Tuesday
11	Wednesday
12	Thursday
13	Friday
14	Saturday
15	Sunday

Seems like only yesterday

My lucky day

Garden fêtes aren't so popular these days, but I loved them when I was growing up in Gainsborough in Lincolnshire. This picture shows me, aged 14, selling buttonholes with my friend Nina Greaves. The buttonholes were made by church ladies with flowers and foliage from their gardens and Nina and I did a brisk trade. People dressed up for the fêtes and we enjoyed helping them to choose the best accessory for their outfit.

Fêtes were held on the vicarage lawn and crowds of people attended to try their skill at hoop-la and skittles, browse the stalls selling bric-a-brac, toys and books or grab a home-made cake before they sold out. Teas were served in the vestry or on tables set out under the trees.

As it happened, this was my lucky day. One of the competitions was 'Guess the Vicar's Weight' and a few weeks earlier when he had come round to have tea with Mum, I'd overheard him confess to being 'just under 18 stone'. My prize was a delicious chocolate cake!

My geometric dress, inspired by the fashion pages of my Jackie magazines, was the nearest thing to Mary Quant that the local Co-op could offer. I loved it. However, I think my Beatle crop was having a bad hair day! I always envied Nina's natural curls. Fifty years on, she still lives in Gainsborough and we remain friends; I hope this picture brings back memories for her too.

Mrs Joy Harris, Peterborough, Cambs

It's a fact

We don't recommend doing this, but should you feel the need to drill a tunnel straight through the earth and jumped in, it would take you 42 minutes 12 seconds to get to the other side. It might well be a better option than commuting.

Turn back time tips

Challenge your brain by brushing your teeth with the other hand, choosing your clothes by touch instead of sight, and taking a different route to the shops. Doing something differently makes your brain build new connections.

Great days out

Black Friars Distillery

The Barbican, Plymouth
This is the oldest gin distillery in England, dating back to 1793. The home of Plymouth gin is where the Pilgrim Fathers most probably spent their last night before departing for the New World. Nowadays, guided tours, tasting sessions and a spot of relaxing in the Refectory cocktail Lounge are all on the cards.
Call 01752 665292 or visit www.plymouthdistillery.com

It made me laugh

A man went to a fancy dress party with a girl on his back.
"I've come as a snail," he announced.
"What about the girl on your back?" the other guests asked.
"That's Michelle."

Yvonne Harding, Devizes, Wiltshire

Recipe of the week

Sausage and Leek Casserole with Chive Mash

Serves: 4
Preparation time: 10 minutes
Cooking time: 30 minutes

3 tbsp olive oil
8 pork sausages
1 Spanish onion, sliced
200g (7oz) leeks, sliced
4 cloves garlic, sliced
2 sticks celery, sliced
Small bunch of sage leaves
200ml (7floz) white wine
400ml (13oz) passata
400ml (13oz) chicken stock
2 bay leaves
Salt and cracked black pepper
800g (1¾lb) potatoes, peeled and quartered
100g (3½oz) butter
300ml (½pt) milk
Salt and cracked white pepper
1 bunch chives, finely chopped
Small bunch flat leaf parsley, chopped

1 Preheat oven to 180°C/350°F/Gas Mark 4. Fry sausages in a casserole dish until golden brown, in two batches if necessary, then remove.
2 Add the onions, leeks, garlic, celery and sage; cook until just browning. Add the wine, stock, passata and bay leaves, then season to taste. Re-introduce the sausages, cover, and cook in the oven for 20 minutes.
3 Meanwhile, cover potatoes with water in a medium pan and bring to the boil. Simmer until cooked (about 20 minutes). Drain then mash with butter and milk. Stir over low heat until piping hot, season to taste, add the chives and set aside.
4 Remove casserole from oven, stir in chopped parsley and serve with mash.
© www.britishleeks.co.uk

16 Monday

17 Tuesday

18 Wednesday

19 Thursday

20 Friday

21 Saturday

22 Sunday

Seems like only yesterday

In days of old

When my grandson asked me to tell him about 'The Olden Days' I was rather taken aback! The Thirties were definitely not always the good old days; the class system divided people and they seldom mixed. Christian names were only used within the family. Even friendly neighbours we'd known for many years were addressed as Mr or Mrs, while strangers at bus stops or in trains never engaged in conversation.

Winters were very cold and icicles hung from burst outside pipes. When indoor pipes froze, they were thawed out with a hot water bottle or a blowlamp. People queued with buckets to collect water from a standpipe in the street.

Once a year, the chimney sweep arrived on his bike with a broom over his shoulder and sack for the soot. Everything in the kitchen was covered with dustsheets. He came in through the back door and asked the children to stand outside and shout when they saw the brush appear at the top of the chimney.

There were few cars on the road, the greengrocer and baker drove vans. The coalman's cart was drawn by an enormous shire horse with a plaited mane. The milkman's cart was also pulled by a horse which used to lean over to nibble at the nearest hedge while it was parked at the side of the road. Occasionally, a gypsy knocked at the door trying to sell bunches of 'lucky' heather or a turbaned Indian would offer a rolled-up mat for sale.

Mrs Sylvia Stilts, Whetstone, London

It's a fact

The Fourth Doctor Who's iconic long, multi-coloured scarf was created by accident. The costume maker misunderstood her instructions for the scarf and knitted all the wool she had been given. However, Tom Baker liked the overly-long scarf, and went on to wear it for the show anyway.

Turn back time tips

Try walking on the grass instead of the pavement, the softer surface could be easier on your joints. Wear well-cushioned shoes, too, if you have to walk a longer distance.

Great days out

Palace House and National Motor Museum

Beaulieu, Hampshire
Built around the gatehouse of Beaulieu Abbey, Palace House is indebted to the Montagu family, who made significant contributions to the adjoining Motor Museum. Not into engines? The ruins of the Abbey have survived in the Palace Gardens to this day, and the house is preserved in Victorian style. Take a House, Abbey or Motoring Tour, or go the whole hog with the Grand Tour, which lasts 2 hours.
Call 01590 612345 or visit www.beaulieu.co.uk

It made me laugh

Q: Why do dogs always put their puppies back in their basket?
A: Because they know they shouldn't leave litter lying around.

Hilda Green, via email

Recipe of the week

Lancashire Cheese and Bramley Apple Pie

Serves: 8
Preparation time: 20 minutes
Cooking time: 40 minutes

500g (1lb) ready-made dessert pastry (rolled out into 2 discs to fit tin)
1kg (2lb) Bramley apples, peeled and roughly chopped
50g (2oz) unsalted butter
2 tbsp soft brown sugar
Pinch or two of black pepper
$^1/_2$ tsp cumin
$^1/_2$ tsp allspice
250g (8oz) thinly sliced Lancashire cheese
2 tsp fresh chopped sage
1 egg, lightly beaten

1 Preheat the oven to 190°C/375°F/Gas Mark 5, and melt the butter in a saucepan.
2 Add the chopped apples, sugar, black pepper and spices, and cook until they begin to soften.
3 Line a 24cm (10in) loose-bottomed baking dish with one disc of pastry. Lay the cheese and fresh sage in the base of the dish. Fill with apple stew, then lightly egg the lip of the pastry dish.
4 Top with the second disc of pastry. Trim edges and crimp to seal. Make a steam hole in the centre and egg well
5 Cook for 35-40 minutes or until golden. Cool slightly before serving.
© Phil Vickery, www.bramleyapples.co.uk

23 Monday

24 Tuesday

25 Wednesday

26 Thursday

27 Friday

28 Saturday

29 Sunday

Seems like only yesterday

Putting on a panto

The estate I lived on when I was growing up in the Forties was a lively place, so when it was proposed that we should put on a children's pantomime, everyone wanted to be in it. It was to be Babes in the Wood and was organised by Auntie May, a community stalwart, aided by Miss Wickens, an elderly maiden lady who could play the piano.

The performance was to be held in the local community hut and the highlight of the evening was a so-called ballet performed by six lads in their early teens. How Auntie May persuaded these streetwise fellows to dress up in home-made ballet outfits and prance around the stage remains a mystery to this day.

When they first made their appearance, there was a momentary hush followed by hoots of laughter as the dancers were recognised. The audience clapped and cheered and shouted encouragement, hoping all the time that the lads would trip over and fall flat on their faces. They became almost hysterical with joy when one boy's shoulder strap broke and he tried in vain to stop his bodice falling down as he performed clumsy pirouettes and arabesques.

The rest of the pantomime passed in a happy dream and the delighted audience clapped anything that came on stage. As for the poor little babes, they could be lost in the wood for ever for all anybody cared.

Mrs Shirley Mew, Dorchester, Dorset

It's a fact

According to the Guinness Book of Records, the world's longest cucumber was grown in Essex, UK in 1986 and measured a whopping 1.1m (3ft 8in). That's enough to make about 44 rounds of cucumber sandwiches – you just need to get hold of the world's largest loaf of bread first.

Turn back time tips

Give yourself an MOT a couple of times a year – check for lumps or bumps, uneven or dis-coloured moles and cuts that won't heal. Report anything unusual to your GP. Even if you think it's probably nothing – it's better to be checked.

Great days out

River Cottage Cookery Courses

Axminster, Devon

Want to get ahead this Christmas? Book in for a course at River Cottage HQ! Even better, a day here would make a fabulous 'experience' present. In Nose to Tail you'll learn how to use all cuts of meat and make delicious terrines. Game Cookery provides the know-how for skinning, jointing, plucking and skinning, and there's a whole host of other options available. Courses generally last from 10am-5pm. **To confirm event dates visit www.rivercottage.net/cookery-school/calendar. Call 01297 630302 or visit www.rivercottage.net/hq**

It made me laugh

A man was charged with murder for killing a man with sandpaper. He told the police: "I don't know what happened – I only intended to rough him up a bit."   **D Powell, Cambridge**

Recipe of the week

Gluten-free Mini Strawberry Frangipanes

Makes: 24
Preparation time: 20 minutes
Cooking time: 12–15 minutes

175g (6oz) strawberries, hulled
75g (3oz) butter, at room temperature
75g (3oz) caster sugar
50g (2oz) self-raising gluten free flour blend
1 medium egg
50g (2oz) ground almonds
Few drops almond extract
40g (1½oz) flaked almonds

1 Preheat the oven to 180°C/350°F/Gas Mark 4. Separate 24 petite fours cases and put into 2 x 12 section mini muffin tins. Halve or quarter the strawberries depending on their size and keep 24 pieces to one side. Chop the rest.
2 Cream the butter and sugar together until soft and pale. Add the gluten free flour and egg and mix until smooth, then stir in the ground almonds and almond extract.
3 Stir in the chopped strawberries then spoon into the cases. Press a strawberry piece into each one, then sprinkle with flaked almonds. Bake for 12-15 minutes until well risen, golden brown and springy.
4 Leave to cool for 10 minutes then transfer to a wire rack to cool completely. Best eaten on the day of making.
© www.seasonalberries.co.uk

30 Monday

1 Tuesday

2 Wednesday

3 Thursday

4 Friday

5 Saturday

6 Sunday

Seems like only yesterday

Just for the record

When I was a teenager, a friend and I went on a picnic and she brought along her little battery-operated portable record player and some records. Although it was only a small player, it was big enough to play LPs (long-playing records for those too young to remember vinyl) as well as singles.

I was so impressed that when Mum asked me what I wanted for Christmas I told her that I would love a portable record player. On Christmas morning I was dismayed to find that instead of what I had asked for, Father Christmas had bought me a huge radiogram – hardly suitable for taking on picnics!

It turned out that Mum had hunted high and low for a portable machine and, unable to find one but not wanting to disappoint me, she had bought the radiogram on hire purchase instead. Of course, not wishing to hurt her feelings, I pretended to be thrilled.

The lyrics of the first single I bought were 'Hoots mon, there's a moose loose about this hoose' sung by Lord Rockingham's XI; when anyone says the words of today's songs are rubbish, I remind them that we had our share in the olden days! My first LP was George Gershwin's Rhapsody in Blue. I played it so often that it's a miracle the stylus didn't go right through it!

This photo of me was taken some years later in Zambia where I had a secretarial job in the government.

Rosy Baxter, Chelmsford, Essex

It made me laugh

There once was a baker named Fred
Whose success never went to his head.
Instead of just looking,
He ate all his cooking,
So it went to his waistline instead.

Beryl Thomas, Motherwell, North Lanarkshire

It's a fact

Not all workers are created equal, in offices or in beehives. Researchers at the University of Illinois found that the stripy insects actually have personalities: some are thrill-seekers, others more timid. A 2011 study even found that agitated honeybees can be pessimistic, showing that, to some extent, bees might have feelings.

Turn back time tips

Just ten minutes a day with your face and hands in the sun during the summer months is all you need to top up your Vitamin D levels. Pop your SPF on afterwards to protect your skin from damaging UV rays.

Great days out

Antiques for Everyone

NEC, Birmingham, Dec 3-6
Head over to Birmingham for one of the UK's leading Antiques and Decorative fairs; with more than 250 specialist dealers showcasing a wide variety of furniture, art deco, ceramics, porcelain, silver, jewellery, prints, maps, dolls and bears. Enjoy a great day out plus talks from leading antiques experts – and who knows, you might spot a few choice presents while you're there! **Visit www. antiquesforeveryone.com.**

Recipe of the week

Beer-infused Christmas Pudding

Serves: 8-10
Preparation time: 15 minutes, plus overnight marinating
Cooking time: $4^{1}/_{2}$ hours – including $1^{1}/_{2}$ on the day

350g (12oz) raisins
225g ($7^{1}/_{2}$oz) sultanas
150ml ($^{1}/_{4}$pt) stout
4 tbsp brandy
3 dried figs, chopped
3 dried apricots, chopped
4 ready-to-eat prunes, chopped
30g ($1^{1}/_{4}$oz) almonds, chopped
1 carrot, peeled and grated
1 apple, peeled and grated
175g (6oz) plain flour
2 tsp ground mixed spice
$^{1}/_{2}$ tsp ground cinnamon
175g (6oz) white breadcrumbs
175g (6oz) dark muscovado sugar
2 eggs, beaten
Sprig of holly, a few glacé cherries and icing sugar, to decorate

1 Place the dried fruit, almonds, carrots and apple into a non-metallic bowl. Soak in the stout overnight, covered with clingfilm.
2 Sift flour and spices together. Mix into the fruit mixture, along with breadcrumbs, sugar and eggs. Pour into one large bowl or two smaller ones.
3 Cover the bowl(s) with pleated greaseproof paper, plus pleated foil on top. Secure with string, tied lightly around the top of the bowl.
4 Stand the pudding in a large pan with a tight-fitting lid. Steam for 3 hours, topping up with boiling water as necessary.
5 Repeat steaming process before serving – for 90 minutes or so. Decorate as illustrated.
© www.lettherebebeer.com

December 7 - 13

7 Monday

8 Tuesday

9 Wednesday

10 Thursday

11 Friday

12 Saturday

13 Sunday

Seems like only yesterday

Sticky toffee

My twin brother, John, and I were born just before the war. When we were six years old we were invited to a party given by American soldiers who were stationed at Immingham Dock in Lincolnshire. Our transport for our great adventure to 'America' was an army lorry. We sat on benches in the back and could see the road below whizzing past through the gaps in the wooden floor.

The party passed like a dream with lovely things to eat, a real Christmas tree and Father Christmas himself. He gave me a wooden pull-along dog on wheels and a big bag of toffees. I opened my bag on the way home and some precious toffees were lost through the gaps in the lorry floor. However, we shared what was left with the rest of the family as we relived our memorable party.

One day when my mother was out, my sister decided that she would make us all some toffee. Without permission, she used our sugar ration so when Mother returned home unexpectedly she guiltily rushed out of the door and tipped the pan of warm toffee into the chicken run at the bottom of the garden. The mixture cooled and set hard on the chickens' feet so they looked as though they were wearing toffee clogs!

My sister wasn't very popular that day – neither with our mother or with her younger siblings who had missed out on their promised toffee treat.

Mrs Elizabeth Jackson, Market Rasen, Lincs

It made me laugh

Q: What did the fireman's wife get for Christmas?
A: A ladder in her stocking.

Barbara Jones, Solihull, West Midlands

It's a fact

As anyone who loves a spot of weekend DIY knows, IKEA is a busy place, but did you realise that the chain sells one bookcase somewhere in the world every 10 seconds? Meanwhile, each year Heinz sells two sachets of ketchup for every person on earth.

Turn back time tips

If you want to look younger make blusher your best friend. For skin that's prone to dryness a cream blush will be more forgiving and won't settle into fine lines. Using your fingertips blend a rose or peach toned shade into the apples of your cheeks and finish by tapping a little highlighter along the very top of your cheekbones.

Great days out

Christmas Spectacular Show

Thursford, Fakenham

Did you know that millions of people head to the east each year, to catch this three-hour, toe-tapping triumph, starring a whole host of West End performers? It's the largest Christmas show in the country, featuring pop favourites, carols, choral performances, fabulous dancers and sensational solo performances. Keep the magic alive beforehand with a trip on Santa's Magical Journey for the little ones. **Call 01328 878477 or visit www.thursford.com**

Recipe of the week

Chocolate Roulade with Boozy Blackberries

Serves: 8
Preparation time: 45 minutes
Cooking time: 15 minutes, plus 3-4 hours cooling

200g (7oz) dark chocolate
5 large eggs, separated
175g (6oz) caster sugar, plus extra
50g (2oz) ground hazelnuts
2 tbsp hot water
225g (8oz) blackberries
3 tbsp sloe gin
400ml (14floz) double cream
2 tbsp icing sugar
Chocolate holly leaves (make while berries are soaking) and blackberries, to decorate

1 Preheat oven to 180°C/350°F/Gas Mark 4. Line a 34x23 cm (13½x9½in) tin.
2 Melt chocolate over gently simmering water. Whisk egg whites into peaks. In a separate bowl, whisk egg yolks into sugar until pale. Fold chocolate into yolks, adding hazelnuts and water. Loosen with a little egg white, then fold in the rest.
3 Bake in the tin for 15 minutes. Cover lightly and cool. Soak blackberries in gin for 3 hours minimum.
4 2-3 hours before serving, whip the cream, folding in icing sugar and gin.
5 Place roulade on to sugared baking paper, on top of a damp cloth. Spread cream and blackberries over and roll up, using paper and cloth. Wrap it in the cloth for 3 minutes to set.
6 Transfer to a plate. Finish with chocolate holly leaves (brush clean holly with melted chocolate, chill to set, repeat, then peel away the leaves) and blackberries.
© www.seasonalberries.co.uk

14 Monday

15 Tuesday

16 Wednesday

17 Thursday

18 Friday

19 Saturday

20 Sunday

Seems like only yesterday

Heather, right, with her sister, Yvonne and Uncle Sam

Party animals

Every Christmas my parents tried to fit as many relatives into our house as possible even if it meant standing room only. We all used to enjoy good traditional fun and the people attending the party put on the entertainment. This photo is of my sister and me (in the red dress) with our Uncle Sam who liked nothing better than to make a complete fool of himself! With his trousers rolled up to reveal his long johns, he is pretending to be a ballerina for the party game called Cobblers Out of Work.

We played many different games and the grand finale of the evening was the Beetle Drive. The older generation struggled to keep up with the high speed set by the younger ones – it was all down to shouting 'Beetle!' when a complete beetle had been drawn. Dices were dropped and sometimes lost and there was much shouting of 'Faster!' and 'Come on, shake the dice!' There was also a prize for the person who had drawn the most amusing beetle.

Before supper was served, our Twelve Days of Christmas glasses came out of their box and each couple was given a glass with the words to the song. The best singers were always given the first six days and Uncle Joe had the Five Gold Rings glass as, when it was his turn to sing, he always stood to attention and took his teeth out, which added to the jollity of the occasion.

Heather Devlin, Manchester

It's a fact

A study asking if people were cat or dog fans, plus examining their personalities, found that 'dog people' have similar traits – tending to be eager to please and extroverted, while 'cat people' were more introverted and curious.

Turn back time tips

Boost your circulation by giving yourself a good rub down with your towel after a shower. Rub upwards from your feet towards your heart. Then from your hands to your heart. It will help to keep your skin smooth too.

Great days out

Winter Wonderland

Hyde Park, London
You can't beat a bit of London magic in the run up to Christmas – a generous sprinkling of which you'll find in the Winter Wonderland. Popular attractions include the Ice Kingdom, Giant Observation Wheel (like a mini London Eye) and the world-famous Zippos Circus, plus there's the ice rink for those of us feeling particularly spritely!
Visit www.winterwonderlandlondon.com, where you can sign up to an E-newsletter and keep track of all the latest event developments.

It made me laugh

"We spend too much time together, that's why we get on each other's nerves," a woman moaned to her friend. "He only works one day a year."
"Where on earth did you find a man who works one day a year?" her friend asked.
"I married Santa Claus."
Andrea Hazeldine, Greenford, Middlesex

Recipe of the week

Reindeer Biscuits
Makes: 20
Preparation time: 25 minutes, plus cooling
Cooking time: 12 minutes

100g (3^{1}/$_{2}$oz) butter
175g (6oz) caster sugar
2 eggs
2 egg yolks
50g (2oz) ground almonds
240g (8^{1}/$_{2}$oz) plain flour
Icing:
120g (4^{1}/$_{4}$oz) butter
250g (83/4oz) icing sugar
1–2 tbsp milk
Food colouring, to suit
Edible glitter (optional)

1 Mix the butter and sugar into a creamy paste. Add the eggs and egg yolks, then fold in almonds and flour.
2 Press into a greased tray, to a thickness of about 6mm (^{1}/$_{4}$in). Cook in a preheated oven at 180°C/350°F/Gas Mark 4 for 10–12 minutes. The biscuit mixture is ready when it just starts to colour. Turn out on to a sheet of baking parchment on a flat cool surface.
3 While still warm to touch, use a cutter to press out the shapes, but don't lift them out until completely cooled.
4 Mix the icing ingredients together, adding milk as needed to make a smooth paste.
5 Now, ice the biscuits all over with plain icing, adding edible glitter if liked. Then add a little red food colouring to the remaining icing, spoon into a bag, and pipe on some shiny red noses.
© www.thehappyegg.co.uk

21 Monday

22 Tuesday

23 Wednesday

24 Thursday

25 Friday

26 Saturday

27 Sunday

Seems like only yesterday

Shirley, aged 9, with her sister.

Christmas in the country

Every Christmas we would visit my father's parents who lived in Essex. I vividly remember travelling there on Christmas Eve and looking in the windows of the passing houses with all the lights and decorations.

My grandparents had a small cottage at the back of which was an alleyway leading to a park. The cottage stood in a large quadrangle in which there was a windmill that had once been in use but had by then been taken over by the local boy scouts. When my sister and I played with the twins who lived next door, we used to climb right to the top of the windmill. Sometimes we also played in an old disused quarry. Both would be considered dangerous now, I suppose.

My sister and I slept in a small bedroom that was reached through a door leading to the staircase. Our parents slept in an adjoining room. We used candles at night as the cottage had no electricity, only old-fashioned gas lamps. On Christmas Eve we hung up our stockings which would be filled with simple things such as crayons, pencils and possibly an orange.

There was no television so, apart from listening to the radio, we passed the time by playing bagatelle (a game similar to a pinball machine) while our parents and grandparents played cards.

My grandmother was a cook by trade so we had lovely Christmas dinners cooked on an old kitchen range. Wonderful memories of innocent days!

Shirley Pearce, Wheatley, Oxon

It's a fact

He may be the star of our favourite festive ditty, but poor Rudolph's most famous feature may be a sign of poor health. Norwegian scientists have hypothesised that his distinctive red nose is probably the result of a parasitic infection of his respiratory system. Poor deer!

Turn back time tips

While it's tempting to stick to comfortable colours such as browns, blacks and beige, when worn the wrong way these safe shades can really add on the years. Stick to tailored pieces only in this colour palette and for a youthful feel add pieces with interesting details and team with metallic accessories.

Great days out

Stirling Castle

Stirling, Central Scotland
Come and mingle with costumed performers at Stirling, in the run up to this most special time of year. The magnificent, 16th century Chapel Royal plays host to an annual evening carol concert held by candlelight. Sing to your heart's content after an afternoon at the Great Hall's traditional shopping fayre. **For dates, times and further information call 01786 450000 or visit www.stirlingcastle.gov.uk**

It made me laugh

Q: What do you call someone who is frightened of Christmas?
A: Santaclaustrophobic.
Veronica Friar, Gosport, Hampshire

Recipe of the week

Beer-infused Stuffing

Makes 15-20 balls
Preparation time: 15 minutes, plus overnight marinating
Cooking time: 25 minutes

450g (14oz) lean sausagemeat
175g (6oz) fresh white breadcrumbs
1 Bramley apple, peeled and grated
75g (3oz) dried apricots, finely chopped
2 sticks celery, chopped
100g (3^1/$_2$oz) canned chestnuts, cooked and roughly chopped
1-2 tbsp each of freshly chopped parsley, thyme and chives
300ml (1/2pt) ale
1 tbsp vegetable oil
1 onion, peeled and finely chopped
50g (2oz) smoked bacon pieces
1 large egg, beaten

1 Mix the sausage meat, breadcrumbs, apple, apricots, celery, chestnuts, herbs and ale in a bowl. Cover and leave overnight, stirring occasionally.
2 Heat the oil in a large pan. Sauté the onion and bacon until soft. Add the sausagemeat, stir to break, then add the remaining ingredients. Stir in the egg.
3 Shape the mixture into balls and stuff the turkey neck end with any excess. Bake at 190°C/375°F/Gas Mark 5 for 25 minutes or until golden.
© www.lettherebebeer.com

28 Monday

29 Tuesday

30 Wednesday

31 Thursday

1 Friday

2 Saturday

3 Sunday

Seems like only yesterday

Winter woes

When I wake up on chilly mornings, I remember how much colder it seemed when I was growing up in our little house in East London in the Fifties. We had a coal fire in the living room where we all tended to congregate, even though it took ages to warm the room. Other heating consisted of an inadequate two-bar electric fire in the hall. There was no heating upstairs unless we were ill, when a fire was lit in the grate in the bedroom.

Dad tried to make winter days more enjoyable by taking my sister and me on trips out. These were usually Sunday morning jaunts in our tiny Morris Minor while Mum cooked the Sunday dinner. If we'd had snow, but the roads were navigable, Dad would take us to Epping Forest. Dad, bless him, thought he was giving us a treat but, unfortunately, I have always been a bad traveller and the constant rocking of the car combined with the sight of endless snow on the fields made me feel nauseous.

We also used to visit Whipps Cross ponds if they were frozen over. There were loads of people on the ice and I shudder to think how dangerous this probably was. But in those days this activity was normal so we had no fear as we slid along, pulled by Dad.

Now when the snow comes I watch it from the window of my centrally heated house and I think fondly of my old Dad.

Mrs Patricia Rolfe, Hornchurch, Essex

It's a fact

In an average lifetime, your heart beats around 2.5 billion times. To equal the amount of blood pumped around the body in your life, you'd need to leave the kitchen tap on full blast for 45 years.

Turn back time tips

Take a power nap; 20 minutes is the perfect amount of sleep to recharge your body and brain. Set an alarm for longer and you may wake up feeling groggy and struggle to get to sleep at bedtime.

Great days out

The Lakes Distillery

Bassenthwaite Lake, Cumbria
Cumbria's first whisky distillery for more than 100 years is now open for business, complete with an impressive state-of-the-art Visitor Centre. PLUS they've recently launched their first gin, so it's been a busy few months for the converted Victorian farm. Take tours, taste plenty and enjoy stunning views of the Fells. Cheers, and happy 2016!
Call 01768 776916 or visit
www.lakesdistillery.com

It made me laugh

Two Eskimos sitting in a kayak were chilly, so they lit a fire in the craft. It sank, proving you can't have your kayak and heat it too.

Daphne Moses, Yeovil, Somerset

Recipe of the week

Boozy Party Doughnuts

Makes 10
Preparation time: 15 minutes, plus 30 minutes chilling
Cooking time: 10 minutes

8–10 tsp mincemeat
8 slices thick white bread, with crusts cut off
A little spreading butter
4 tbsp caster sugar
100g (3$^{1}/_{2}$oz) self-raising flour, sifted
150ml ($^{1}/_{4}$pt) ale
Vegetable oil, for deep fat frying

1 Spread one side of bread with very little butter. Spoon 1 tsp mincemeat into the centre.
2 Take a second slice and press and seal the two slices together. Cut with a star or round cutter and chill for 30 minutes.
3 Make batter by mixing the sugar and flour. Whisk in the ale until it becomes thick.
4 Heat oil to 180˚C/350˚F. Cover the chilled bread shapes with batter, then fry until golden brown on both sides.
5 Drain the doughnuts on crumpled kitchen roll. Dust with sugar before serving.
© www.lettherebebeer.com

2014 Year-to-view calendar

January

M		6	13	20	27	
Tu		7	14	21	28	
W	1	8	15	22	29	
Th	2	9	16	23	30	
F	3	10	17	24	31	
Sa	4	11	18	25		
Su	5	12	19	26		

February

M		3	10	17	24	
Tu		4	11	18	25	
W		5	12	19	26	
Th		6	13	20	27	
F		7	14	21	28	
Sa	1	8	15	22		
Su	2	9	16	23		

March

M		3	10	17	24	31
Tu		4	11	18	25	
W		5	12	19	26	
Th		6	13	20	27	
F		7	14	21	28	
Sa	1	8	15	22	29	
Su	2	9	16	23	30	

April

M		7	14	21	28	
Tu	1	8	15	22	29	
W	2	9	16	23	30	
Th	3	10	17	24		
F	4	11	18	25		
Sa	5	12	19	26		
Su	6	13	20	27		

May

M		5	12	19	26	
Tu		6	13	20	27	
W		7	14	21	28	
Th	1	8	15	22	29	
F	2	9	16	23	30	
Sa	3	10	17	24	31	
Su	4	11	18	25		

June

M		2	9	16	23	30
Tu		3	10	17	24	
W		4	11	18	25	
Th		5	12	19	26	
F		6	13	20	27	
Sa		7	14	21	28	
Su	1	8	15	22	29	

July

M		7	14	21	28	
Tu	1	8	15	22	29	
W	2	9	16	23	30	
Th	3	10	17	24	31	
F	4	11	17	25		
Sa	5	12	19	26		
Su	6	13	20	27		

August

M		4	11	18	25	
Tu		5	12	19	26	
W		6	13	20	27	
Th		7	14	21	28	
F	1	8	15	22	29	
Sa	2	9	16	23	30	
Su	3	10	17	24	31	

September

M	1	8	15	22	29	
Tu	2	9	16	23	30	
W	3	10	17	24		
Th	4	11	18	25		
F	5	12	19	26		
Sa	6	13	20	27		
Su	7	14	21	28		

October

M		6	13	20	27	
Tu		7	14	21	28	
W	1	8	15	22	29	
Th	2	9	16	23	30	
F	3	10	17	24	31	
Sa	4	11	18	25		
Su	5	12	19	26		

November

M		3	10	17	24	
Tu		4	11	18	25	
W		5	12	19	26	
Th		6	13	20	27	
F		7	14	21	28	
Sa	1	8	15	22	29	
Su	2	9	16	23	30	

December

M	1	8	15	22	29	
Tu	2	9	16	23	30	
W	3	10	17	24	31	
Th	4	11	18	25		
F	5	12	19	26		
Sa	6	13	20	27		
Su	7	14	21	28		

2016 Year-to-view calendar

January

M		4	11	18	25	
Tu		5	12	19	26	
W		6	13	20	27	
Th		7	14	21	28	
F	1	8	15	22	29	
Sa	2	9	16	23	30	
Su	3	10	17	24	31	

February

M	1	8	15	22	29	
Tu	2	9	16	23		
W	3	10	17	24		
Th	4	11	18	25		
F	5	12	19	26		
Sa	6	13	20	27		
Su	7	14	21	28		

March

M		7	14	21	28	
Tu	1	8	15	22	29	
W	2	9	16	23	30	
Th	3	10	17	24	31	
F	4	11	18	25		
Sa	5	12	19	26		
Su	6	13	20	27		

April

M		4	11	18	25	
Tu		5	12	19	26	
W		6	13	20	27	
Th		7	14	21	28	
F	1	8	15	22	29	
Sa	2	9	16	23	30	
Su	3	10	17	24		

May

M		2	9	16	23	30
Tu		3	10	17	24	31
W		4	11	18	25	
Th		5	12	19	26	
F		6	13	20	27	
Sa		7	14	21	28	
Su	1	8	15	22	29	

June

M		6	13	20	27	
Tu		7	14	21	28	
W	1	8	15	22	29	
Th	2	9	16	23	30	
F	3	10	17	24		
Sa	4	11	18	25		
Su	5	12	19	26		

July

M		4	11	18	25	
Tu		5	12	19	26	
W		6	13	20	27	
Th		7	14	21	28	
F	1	8	15	22	29	
Sa	2	9	16	23	30	
Su	3	10	17	24	31	

August

M	1	8	15	22	29	
Tu	2	9	16	23	30	
W	3	10	17	24	31	
Th	4	11	18	25		
F	5	12	19	26		
Sa	6	13	20	27		
Su	7	14	21	28		

September

M		5	12	19	26	
Tu		6	13	20	27	
W		7	14	21	28	
Th	1	8	15	22	29	
F	2	9	16	23	30	
Sa	3	10	17	24		
Su	4	11	18	25		

October

M		3	10	17	24	31
Tu		4	11	18	25	
W		5	12	19	26	
Th		6	13	20	27	
F		7	14	21	28	
Sa	1	8	15	22	29	
Su	2	9	16	23	30	

November

M		7	14	21	28	
Tu	1	8	15	22	29	
W	2	9	16	23	30	
Th	3	10	17	24		
F	4	11	18	25		
Sa	5	12	19	26		
Su	6	13	20	27		

December

M		5	12	19	26	
Tu		6	13	20	27	
W		7	14	21	28	
Th	1	8	15	22	29	
F	2	9	16	23	30	
Sa	3	10	17	24	31	
Su	4	11	18	25		

RELAX & UNWIND

PICS: REX FEATURES

Gran's got talent!

BY: SUSAN WRIGHT

Jayne's mum is convinced she has the X–factor

Jayne rushed into the hall when she heard the sound of a key in the front door. "Oh, it's only you," she said as her husband stepped inside.

"Sorry to disappoint you," Tom replied cheerfully. "Who were you expecting? George Clooney?"

"I was hoping you were Mum. She's gone missing?" Tom frowned. "Gone missing?"

"I came home from work and the house was as quiet as the grave and I can't find her anywhere," Jayne wailed. "She hasn't even left a note!"

"Odd," Tom put down his suitcase and grinned at his wife. "Still, at least I'll be able to watch TV in peace for once. It's hard to concentrate with your mum belting out 'New York, New York' in her room."

"How can you think about television? I'm worried sick. She's never been out when I get home from work."

"It is a bit strange," Tom admitted as he sank down on the sofa. "Maybe, she's gone out on a date. She had a mysterious phone call last week. I meant to tell you about it, but you were in the bath at the time."

"A mysterious phone call?"

"Yes, it sounded as though she was arranging to meet someone called Simon."

"Simon?" Jayne stared in amazement. "Oh my goodness, it must have been Simon Cowell!"

"THE Simon Cowell?"

"Yes. She got herself all worked up because older people never win The X-Factor so she wrote to Simon Cowell to suggest he did a show just for them!"

"Oh right. But it's unlikely he'd have taken any notice of that."

"Who knows?" Jayne shrugged.

Tom looked thoughtful. "Well, she certainly seemed very excited when she came off the phone. Dashed upstairs and did another run through of 'New York, New York'. It would be brilliant if your mum was on television, wouldn't it?"

Jayne looked horrified. "No, it wouldn't. It would be very embarrassing. I don't think she's that good a

> ## "It's hard to concentrate with your mum belting out 'New York, New York'"

singer, Tom. Everyone would be making fun of her."

"No, they wouldn't."

Jayne slumped down on the sofa as a thought struck her. "You might be right about Simon Cowell. She's bought herself some new clothes. I took a cup of tea up to her the other night and she was standing in front of the mirror wearing a black mini skirt, a halter-neck top and four-inch high heels!"

Tom laughed. "She must have looked amazing!"

"She looked ridiculous," Jayne replied. "She had tons of make-up on as well. I don't get it, Tom, she's acting like a teenager. When she first moved in with us, she was miserable because Dad had died, but recently she has changed."

"Mmm. Well, maybe she felt that time was running out."

Jayne looked at her watch and sighed. "Oh, I wish she'd come home. I'm so worried. She would have killed me if I'd gone out without telling her when I was young."

"It's only twenty past eight," Tom pointed out.

"Yes, but I don't know where she is! Do you think I should phone the police?"

"No, I don't," Tom said, giving her a hug. "I think you should just sit there and enjoy the silence. She'll start singing again as soon as she comes in."

Jayne managed a smile. "That's true."

Tom rolled his eyes. "You'd think she might have learned more than one song in 74 years."

"Well, she's trying to perfect it, I suppose. Oh, I wish I knew what's going on! Do you think she has met up with Simon Cowell?"

Tom shrugged. "I don't know, love."

At that moment, they heard the front door opening.

"Mum?" Jayne called out. "Where on earth have you been? I was worried sick when I came home and found you missing."

"I wasn't missing," her mother said. "I've been singing for Simon."

Jayne swallowed. "And what did he think of you?"

Betty grinned: "He thought I was amazing." She kicked off her four-inch heels. "Mind you, I didn't have much competition. Out of four of us, one woman had to drop out because her replacement hip was playing up and another one had a heart

ILLUSTRATION: KATE DAVIES

attack last night."

"Oh dear," Jayne said. "So there were just the two of you?"

"Yes, and I won," Betty beamed, holding up a bottle of Champagne.

Jayne's jaw dropped. "So when are you going to be on television?"

"Television?"

"Yes," Tom said. "I can't wait to see you performing for Simon Cowell."

Betty frowned. "I wrote to him, but he never replied."

Tom looked puzzled. "So who is this Simon?"

"Simon Smith," Betty explained. "He runs a pub

where they do karaoke. I persuaded him to have a competition for the over-70s."

Tom grinned at his wife's visible relief.

"It was brilliant," Betty went on. "I'm going to be in the local paper and somebody filmed me as well!"

"Filmed you?"

"A chap from a TV company. Says I've got talent."

"Really?"

"Yes, really! He's sending the film to some people."

"Like who?" Jayne asked, torn between astonishment and admiration.

"Oh, people in the media," Betty replied breezily, heading to the kitchen with her bottle of Champagne. "Including Simon Cowell!"

Perfect partners

Match the fictional heroine to her timeless handsome hero

1 Scarlett O'Hara	A Harry Potter
2 Frances 'Baby' Housman	B Henry Higgins
3 Lady	C Fitzwilliam Darcy
4 Bonnie Parker	D Tarzan
5 Eliza Doolittle	E Jack Duckworth
6 Cathy Earnshaw	F Clark Kent
7 Ginny Weasley	G Rhett Butler
8 Morticia Addams	H Othello
9 Bella Swan	I Shrek
10 Vera Duckworth	J Heathcliffe
11 Lois Lane	K Rick Blaine
12 Barbie	L Gomez Addams
13 Ilsa Lund	M Mark Darcy
14 Maid Marian	N Johnny Castle
15 Elizabeth Bennett	O Clyde Barrow
16 Cinderella	P Ken
17 Desdemona	Q Tramp
18 Jane	R Edward Cullen
19 Princess Fiona	S Robin Hood
20 Bridget Jones	T Prince Charming

PIC: REX FEATURE

Answers: 1=G, 2=N, 3=Q, 4=O, 5=B 6=J, 7=A, 8=L, 9=R, 10=E, 11=F, 12=P, 13=K, 14=S, 15=C, 16=T, 17=H, 18=D, 19=I, 20=M

Box of memories... chat shows

Talk-shows gave us some of TV's most revealing moments

Hylda Baker, playing it for laughs on Russell Harty's show

PIC: REX FEATURES

Far from being easy viewing, the earliest chat show on TV, Face to Face, probed deep into the psyche of the celebrities who were interviewed by the formidable John Freeman. What's My Line? panellist Gilbert Harding was reduced to tears by Freeman – that would never happen with cuddly Graham Norton!

By the time Joan Bakewell reached our screens as a presenter of Late Night Line-Up, the talk-show format was more relaxed, although serious subject matters were still at the forefront, focusing on the arts and the media. Much more lighthearted was Dee Time, an early evening show hosted by DJ Simon Dee who fooled around, told bad jokes and chatted to showbiz personalities before driving off in an E-type Jaguar with a

glamorous blonde at his side.

The most famous chat show host of all was, of course, Michael Parkinson. He interviewed more than 1,000 stars in 361 shows, but the one that everyone remembers is Emu the ostrich who attacked Parky in a most undignified manner. Another puppet guest, Miss Piggy, responded more positively to Parky's charm and what she flirtily called his 'bedroom eyes'.

Being a chat show host on live TV was a risky business. In 1980, Russell Harty's guest, singer Grace Jones, bashed him over the head for ignoring her. On another occasion, The Who's drummer Keith Moon stripped down to his underpants. No wonder Harty's show was billed as 'television's most

unpredictable half-hour'.

The best chat show hosts managed to look at ease whatever their guests got up to and Terry Wogan was a dab hand at this – despite falling over on the very first edition of Wogan (whoops!) Terry was perfectly sober, unlike footballer George Best, who'd clearly had more than a few 'little drinkies' before his appearance on a later edition of the show.

The most memorably drunk guest was Oliver Reed who lurched on to Michael Aspel's Saturday night show, Aspel and Company, sang Wild One and had the cheek to accuse another guest, Clive Anderson, of being tipsy. Happily, unfazed by this experience, Clive went on to host his own show, Saturday Night Clive.

"We used woodworl

Beryl Ruth faced many challenges trying to teach cookery after the war...

"**W**hat are we making next week, Miss?" asked the 20 eager-faced girls who stood by my desk in the dilapidated cookery room.

I began teaching cookery in 1946. Food was rationed and I had to work out what I was to teach for a month so that I could apply for the coupons from the Ministry of Food to buy the items from my registered shop. There was always a generous allowance of cheese – 4ozs per child per month. Plenty of flour, dried egg and dried milk, too. Meat, including sausage, corned beef and offal was 1 shilling (5p) per month. We became experts with soya flour, oatmeal, herrings and tinned pilchards – mackerel in breadcrumbs became part of our staple diet! Baking was difficult with the lack of sugar, but we did make rock cakes and raspberry buns from time to time.

After leaving Bath Domestic Science College, where I trained for three years, it was quite a shock to be appointed to a school that had no proper cookery room. I used the woodwork room in the mornings – the boys did woodwork in the afternoons. We placed our old pastry boards across the woodwork benches, and wound in the vices (when we remembered!) My shins were always black and blue at the end of a lesson!

Equipment was practically non-existent. Two old gas stoves, one stone sink, a few chipped yellow earthenware mixing

bowls, jugs and some tin plates. Cutlery was not stainless and so each morning, if the girls had not dried it thoroughly the day before, it would have become rusty. There was no blackboard, no books, no refrigerator, no cupboard to keep the few utensils in and nowhere to keep food, so everything had to be used up by the end of each lesson.

The woodwork master, Mr Topliss, kindly put a few shelves up for me to store the bowls, boxes of cutlery and the recipe cards I had specially made. The shelves were then covered with tea towels to prevent them from gathering dust from the woodwork shavings in the afternoon.

Although hard work, I enjoyed the teaching here, since the girls and their parents were so appreciative of our humble dishes.

I eventually moved on to a better equipped school in 1950, where I converted three rooms into a self-contained flat, which the girls loved cleaning and entertaining staff at lunch time. It was at this school that I got my first washing machine. No more using a rubbing board and scrubbing brush as I had to before!

In 1955 I moved to the grammar school at the request of the headmistress to start the O-Level cookery class. Again, it was not a

rooms as kitchens!"

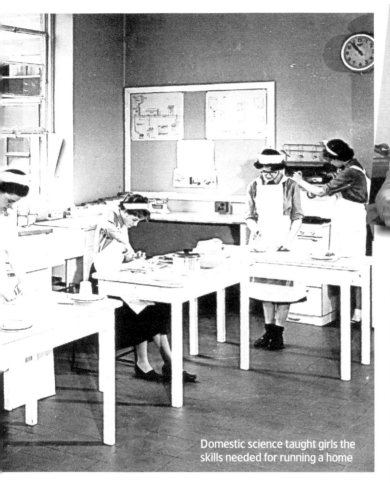

Domestic science taught girls the skills needed for running a home

Beryl translated her home economics knowledge into book form

domestic science.

Although teaching O and A-Level was very rewarding, it was also very restricting. I wanted to do much more than just teach cookery. So when I was appointed to the technical block of a new school I was able to expand the subject. I began transforming what was cookery to home economics. I was appointed as examiner for the West Midlands, and later became Chief Examiner for the West Midlands and Lancashire.

very well-equipped room, and for the first O-Level exam I borrowed dishes from my aunt, as well as raiding my own home for suitable dishes, tablecloths and napkins for the girls to present their dishes to the examiner. After this I was allowed to equip a new room especially for the subject. I chose to make five small kitchens, each one equipped differently. One was the plastic kitchen (everything plastic). Not always successful, especially when one girl decided to prove the bread she was making in the oven and the dish and dough disintegrated into the shelves. I spent half an hour trying to clear it up!

The Pyrex kitchen also did not appeal, since the glass dishes and rolling pin could easily break. The country kitchen had mainly wood and stoneware items, while the Cornish kitchen had the lovely blue and white earthenware items. The economy kitchen had enamel and aluminium equipment. Each kitchen had the cost of each item displayed on the door of the unit so that the girls could see which was the cheapest or most expensive. While at this grammar school I embarked on A-Level domestic science, and three of my pupils went on to take the exam, finally going to college and becoming teachers of

Now I could really get stuck in! I broadened the curriculum to include shopping, not only buying food but also furnishing a home. I taught child care, money management and how to dress and conduct yourself at job interviews. I eventually began to write my own books on the subject, and many teachers came in to watch my lessons.

In 1980 I was forced to retire through ill health but I have fond memories of teaching home economics, and despair at the thought that such a vital subject is no longer taught in schools.

Across the board

BY: KEITH HAVERS

Geoff's grandson checkmates him every time!

Geoff asked: "So, have you thought about what it will be like when your baby brother arrives?"

His grandson, Mason, paused in the middle of their game of chess as if considering the question.

"Cat got your tongue?" Geoff prompted as Mason smiled and took the black knight with his white pawn.

"Checkmate, Granddad."

Geoff rubbed his chin. His enquiry had partly been intended as a distraction but his ploy had backfired and caused him to lose his own concentration. "Hmmm. Not bad for a seven year old," he admitted.

"Want another game?"

"Er, not now, son. What about answering my question. You are looking forward to the baby coming, aren't you?"

"Suppose so."

Geoff wondered if the boy's parents had sat the lad down and had a talk about how the new arrival would affect him. He suspected they were so caught up in the euphoria of the imminent birth that they hadn't given it much thought. It was only natural. Time for Granddad to step in.

"What has your mum told you?"

"She says I'll have to start doing more things for myself when the baby is here."

"Oh? Like what?"

"Like getting my stuff ready for school and putting my toys away."

"That doesn't sound too bad. Sort of things you should be doing at your age anyway."

"Suppose."

Geoff could tell something was still troubling the boy, but sensed it would take a bit of coaxing to

When he had first taught him the game Geoff had deliberately let his grandson win

get it out of him. He said: "I've changed my mind. Go on then – set 'em up again. But this time be prepared for a beating!"

He watched the intense look on Mason's face as he lined up the chess pieces. When he had first taught him the game Geoff had deliberately let his grandson win now and again, but these days he had to be on his mettle.

"Are you worried that Mum and Dad won't be able to spend as much time with you when they have a baby to look after? Your gran and I will still do the same things with you as we do now."

"I know you will, Granddad."

They played in silence. Geoff knew it wasn't any use trying to make Mason talk if he didn't want to. The boy would open up in his own time.

"Granddad?"

"Yes, son?"

"Will I still get Christmas and birthday presents?"

Geoff chuckled. "Of course you will. Whatever made you think you wouldn't?"

"Mum and Dad said we couldn't afford a holiday this year with all the things they need to buy for the baby. And if they can't afford a holiday…"

"Christmas and birthdays are special. They'll always have enough money for those."

"Really?"

"And you never know – the new baby might bring you a present when he gets here. Just as a way of saying hello."

Mason gave his granddad a quizzical look.

Geoff explained: "When your great uncle Roger was born, my parents brought him home from hospital in a basket. When I looked in the basket there was a box of building bricks with my name on it."

Mason screwed up his face in disbelief. "But the baby didn't buy them, did he? It was your mum and dad that did it."

"I was only three at the time so I didn't know any better. My parents did it just to show they still loved me even though they had another little one to look after."

This explanation appeared to satisfy the lad's

ILLUSTRATION: KATE DAVIES

"The new baby might bring you a present when he gets here"

curiosity. He turned his attention back to the board, moved his bishop three squares diagonally and beamed at his grandfather. "Checkmate."

When the baby was born, Geoff stood in the doorway of the nursery and watched as parents, big brother and grandma gathered around the cot to coo at the latest addition to the family.

On a prompt from his mum, Mason lifted the crochet shawl to find a package at the bottom of the cot. He pulled off the wrapping paper to find the DVD of his favourite animated film. Geoff winked as the boy looked across at him and smiled.

"What are you doing standing over there?" Grandma asked. "Don't you want to say hello to your new grandson?"

"Yes, come on, Granddad. He wants to meet you," Mason said.

Geoff stepped across and peered into the crib. He blinked back a tear at his first sight of the crumpled pink face and wisp of black hair.

"What's this, Granddad?" Mason asked, pulling a box out from under the cot. "It's got your name on it."

Geoff peeled back the wrapping to reveal the coloured illustration on a box lid. He glanced round at the smiling faces. His daughter said: "It's from all of us."

"And the baby," interrupted Mason.

"We thought you might have felt a bit left out while we've all been preoccupied with this little one. And you've spent a lot of time with Mason, so this is a thank-you present."

"There was no need! I don't know what to say…"

"It's a chess computer," Mason said with a cheeky grin. "The baby thought you would like it."

"And from what I hear," grandma chipped in, "you need the practice!"

Children's classics

How much do you
know about literature
from your childhood?

1 What were the names of the Little Women?
A) Megan, Jo, Bethany and Allie
B) Meg, Jo, Beth and Amy
C) Maggie, Joan, Beth and Amy

2 What did the Railway Children wave in the air to stop a train?
A) Their socks
B) Their gloves
C) Their petticoats

3 What does BFG stand for?
A) Big Friendly Giant
B) Buy One Get One Free
C) Big Fat Giant

4 What does Mary Lennox discover behind a wall?
A) A secret garden
B) A secret society
C) A secret affair

5 Which friend of Winnie-the-Pooh has a sign on the door reading: 'PLES RING IF AN RNSER IS REQIRD' and 'PLEZ CNOKE IF AN RNSR IS NOT REQID'
A) Eeyore
B) Rabbit
C) Owl

6 How do Pongo and Missus locate their missing puppies?
A) Using twilight barking
B) With their sense of smell
C) With a map

7 What is Harry Potter's pet owl called?
A) Hedgehog
B) Hedwig
C) Hogwig

8 Which of the children in Charlie and the Chocolate Factory ends up in a river of chocolate?
A) Veruca Salt
B) Augustus Gloop
C) Mike Teavee

9 Only one character appears in all seven of the Narnia books, who?
A) Aslan
B) Susan
C) Edmund

10 What do the characters Babe and Wilbur have in common?
A) They are both left handed
B) They are both cats
C) They are both pigs

11 In Treasure Island the pirate Long John Silver is missing which part of his anatomy?
A) An eye
B) A hand
C) A leg

12 What are the names of the Fossil girls in Ballet Shoes?
A) Pauline, Petrova and Posy
B) Polly, Pauly and Poppy
C) Princess, Poppet and Peppy

13 What do Sophie and her mummy buy in case the Tiger Who Came To Tea returns?
A) A lock for the door
B) A tiger-sized trap
C) A tin of tiger food

14 Which game must Alice play with the Queen of Hearts?
A) Croquet
B) Golf
C) Badminton

15 Who said: "To die will be an awfully big adventure"?
A) Tinkerbell
B) Peter Pan
C) Wendy

Answers: 1)b 2)c 3)a 4)a 5)c 6)a 7)b 8)b 9)a 10)c 11)c 12)a 13)c 14)a 15)b

Box of memories... police dramas

The long arm of the law, whether US or UK, had us in its grip!

Just one more thing from the ramshackle Columbo... but he always got his man or woman

PIC REX FEATURES

Greeting us with a friendly 'Evenin' all', PC (later Sergeant) George Dixon (Jack Warner) made us feel we were in safe hands so long as there were decent bobbies like him on the beat. Writer Ted Willis based his stories on those of a real policeman who had been stationed in London's East End, but crime in Dock Green was pretty tame compared with Newtown where Constables 'Fancy' Smith (Brian Blessed) and Bert Lynch (James Ellis) patrolled the mean streets in a Ford Zephyr.

In Z Cars they brought a gritty Liverpudlian realism to police drama as well as introducing the car as an essential member of the cast. As DI Jack Regan in The Sweeney, John Thaw screeched around the streets of London in a Ford Consul or Granada, but years later, as Inspector Morse, he drove more sedately around Oxford in a classic Jaguar Mark 2. Not to be outdone in the car department, Bergerac (John Nettles) negotiated Jersey's country lanes in a natty burgundy Triumph Roadster.

Across the Atlantic, Lieutenant Columbo (Peter Falk) drove a battered Peugeot that went with his trademark shabby mac. While Columbo fought crime in Los Angeles, the baddies of New York went in fear of a bald, lollipop-loving cop known as Kojak (Telly Savalas) whose catchphrase was 'Who loves ya, baby?'

It was said that Kojak sucked a lollipop as a substitute for a cigarette at a time when the dangers of smoking were becoming better known. No such inhibitions affected Commisaire Jules Maigret who visibly relished lighting his pipe at least once in every episode. He was played by Rupert Davies, a confirmed pipe-smoker in real life.

In the Eighties, two women cops graced our screens. In Juliet Bravo Stephanie Turner was Inspector Jean Darblay who was in charge of a police station in the northern town of Hartley. Down south, DI Maggie Forbes (Jill Gascoine) was based in the Seven Dials area of London for The Gentle Touch. As Jill couldn't drive, she sat in a car towed by a camera truck – a change from her male predecessors!

The bright lights of

Ellie Arlen and her classmates got a taste of the London lifestyle during a once-in-a-lifetime school trip...

It was 1955, and I'd reached the age of 12 before I first got to spend a whole weekend away from my home and family. But what a weekend to remember!

Due to the sheer teeth-gritting courage of our teachers, my class – 1A – were taken on a trip to London to broaden our horizons with a slice of culture and sophistication. Just imagine a coach-load of excited, almost teenagers, many of whom had never even ventured out of Yorkshire before, heading for the bright light of the metropolis!

We stayed in a hotel that was, admittedly, a bit down-at-heel, but for us the location was thrilling – somewhere 'up West'. On our very first evening we were taken out to a show at the Adelphi Theatre in the Strand.

The show our teachers had thought 'appropriate' was a review named 'The Talk of the Town'. It starred the comedian Jimmy Edwards. Remember Jimmy, with his larger-than-life presence, handlebar moustache and comic 'Oompa, oompa, stick it up your jumper' performances on the tuba and trombone? We already knew and loved him as Pa Glum in the radio show 'Take It From Here'. Our teachers must have figured that comedy, combined with the opportunity to see a big radio star in the flesh, would appeal to us. It did – but we got more than they'd bargained for!

We stared goggle-eyed as the dancers – The Talk of the Town

London's West End offered bright lights and excitement

Lovelies and The John Tiller Girls – displayed more glamorous flesh than we'd seen in our entire lives, in routines with names like 'The Kute Kittens'. What's more, some of the jokes in the show came across – to our sheltered minds – as, well, smutty! How gleefully we eyed our teachers' discomfort, as they unsuccessfully battled to bite back their laughter. It really upped our enjoyment to discover that we'd inadvertently been taken to something that (by Fifties standards) might be classed as a bit risqué!

The following day we took in some of the landmarks, which were still soot-blackened and drab compared with today. But what stands out in my memory is not my first sighting of Big Ben or Buckingham Palace, nor even a tour of The Tower of London. It was having lunch at a Lyons Corner House. The Corner Houses were renowned for offering reliable menus at reasonable prices, and serving them in far grander surroundings than any of us had eaten in before. I remember we were told how much we could spend, then handed the responsibility of ordering for ourselves (though advised that, in London, it was polite to have a starter first, before tucking into sausage and mash!)

That evening, in a whirl of non-stop experience-gathering, it

the big city

STOLL
THEATRE
KINGSWAY · W·C·2

JACK HYLTON presents

ALFRED DRAKE
in
KISMET
A Musical Arabian Night

with
DORETTA MORROW
and
JOAN DIENER

Programme
Sixpence

Kismet was the red-hot theatre ticket of the year

A young Ellie (inset) had her first weekend away from home at the age of 12

was out to the theatre yet again. This time it was the magnificent Stoll theatre, in Kingsway (now, tragically, demolished). We were overflowing with anticipation.

Finding it difficult to obtain advance tickets for the Saturday night, our teachers had taken a gamble. They'd booked us into a show from America, that was still relatively unknown over here. How the gamble paid off! The show turned out to be the musical 'Kismet', based on 'Tales of the Arabian Nights', with tunes adapted from music by the Russian composer Borodin. It

starred big names from Broadway and, on its recent opening, it had become an overnight smash hit.

Tunes from the show were constantly on the radio, and record sales were booming. We already knew the words to 'Baubles, Bangles and Beads' and the hit song of the show, 'A Stranger in Paradise'. From our seats up in the 5/6s, our ears filled by haunting music, we feasted our eyes on the magical sets, representing the Broadway versions of old Baghdad, and felt fit to burst with pride and arm-pinching incredulity that we were there. Us! Class 1A from a little mining town in Yorkshire, in possession of the hottest tickets in town!

Then, to top it all, as we formed a crocodile to wind our way back to the hotel, a rumour ran round that somebody had spotted the pop singer Alma Cogan getting

into a limousine. Allegedly, she'd waved! Unsurprisingly, she'd not been wearing one of her trademark sequined stage frocks with the voluminous petticoats, but was sensibly dressed in an oatmeal-coloured suit, which we girls prided ourselves on knowing was very on trend. We took on an air of worldliness and sophistication as we made our way back to the hotel through the neon-lit streets of London, which we were already starting to call our own.

London has changed so much since the spring of 1955, and the 12 year olds of today would scoff at our innocence. Yet, whenever I visit London, I still get a repeat injection of that youthful adrenalin.

Looking back, I see how fortunate we were to have had such brave and enterprising teachers. They certainly gave us the time of our lives. What's more, they got us all back home to Yorkshire safe and sound – although some of the girls, I included, had temporarily acquired a more sassy, potentially annoying 'London' walk!

Chatting up is

BY: MADDIE PURSLOW

It's a funny old world but true facts could lead Tony to his true love

When I was a teenager (a long time ago, I grant you), my brother and I used to play the True Fact game. It kept us amused on many a boring Sunday afternoon and we still like to play it when we have a family get-together.

I must explain that our so-called true facts are neither true nor facts, but the more outrageous they are, the more we like them. Things like 'Leonardo da Vinci invented the stapler' or 'kilts were first worn by Buddhist monks'. There is only one rule, which is that you have to end your statement with the words, 'True Fact'. It's a bit like Simon Says, only sillier.

Now here's the thing; when I first met Pamela at a dinner dance, I instantly reverted to being the teenage me. You see, I'm rubbish at talking to women – always have been. I never know what to say to them. And if they are pretty – well, I'm even worse. So I always go for a joke. Most of the time, it doesn't work. I'm met with a blank stare or that hair flick thing women do which means they're embarrassed and wish you would push off.

But Pamela was different. Pamela laughed. We had been chatting for a while when I decided to try her with one of my True Facts. "Did you know that John Wayne was really good at crochet? True fact!"

She looked at me for a moment, then burst out laughing. "That is just not true!"

"It is, it is!" I protested. "And did you know that China has the most tap dancers in the world? True fact."

She tilted her head to one side and said: "Okay, it's a crazy world. I'm an American so, trust me, I know that. But that is crazy?"

"You come across stuff like this all the time so some of it could be true and we just don't know it yet. Go on, you give it a try."

"Oh, I don't know. This is British humour, I'm not sure I can do it."

"Just let your mind go," I urged. "Say whatever comes into your head."

After a pause, Pamela held up her hands in defeat. "I can't! No – wait. Give me a subject. That might help."

"Sharks. Sharks are always good for a laugh."

"Sharks," she repeated. "Okay, here goes. Sharks are the only sea creatures that have gardens. True fact."

"That's it! True fact!" I said. "Perfect. Now did you know that Jerry Lee Lewis could eat fifty onion rings at one sitting? True fact."

And so it began; our three fantastic months of true facts and, for me, true love. I was totally captivated by my southern belle. We got along so easily – there was never any awkwardness or silly tactics. We just clicked.

Then she hit me right between the eyes with her own true fact. She was going back to America because she had promised her family she would only stay for 12 months. Pamela had to fly home, back to her old life.

I was lost. The thought of returning to long nights with just me and Chairman Meow, my cat, for company was not a happy prospect. I adored Pamela and had been seriously thinking of asking her to marry me. Even the Chairman liked her, and he didn't like anybody. Now it was all over and I would be just another lonely bloke who couldn't muster a good chat-up line.

What we needed, I told the Chairman, was a plan.

A week before Pamela was due to leave I asked her round to dinner. I'm not much of a cook, but I thought I'd treat her to my signature dish, toad-in-the-hole, followed by spotted dick for pudding. I reasoned this menu was typically English and good for a laugh, if nothing else.

Everything was prepared, including my last-ditch plan to win her round.

We met for a pre-dinner drink in my local, then back to my flat. As we entered, I turned on the light and there was a large bunch of flowers with an envelope attached. Pamela stopped. "For me?" she asked.

Feigning innocence, I said: "I don't know. Nothing to do with me. Why don't you open the envelope and see."

I'm rubbish at talking to women... I never know what to say to them

hard to do

ILLUSTRATION: KATE DAVIES

I'm not much of a cook, but I thought I'd treat her to my signature dish

Suspiciously, she took out the neatly typed note. "This had better not be some sort of gag," she warned.

"No, no. I promise."

She read aloud: "Dear Pamela, please don't go back to America. Stay here with me and Tony because we both love you very much. From Chairman Meow."

For a moment she said nothing and I began to get that old sinking feeling. I'd messed things up again. Even with the best of intentions, I always manage to do the wrong thing.

But then a smile crept across her face and she threw her arms around my neck and kissed me.

"What's that for? The flowers are from Chairman Meow."

"Sure, I know that. I just felt like kissing you, that's all."

I teased: "Aren't you just a bit curious how the Chairman managed it?"

She flapped her hand dismissively: "No, of course not. All cats secretly know how to type. True fact."

What's the connection?

Answer these general knowledge questions and then work out what the answers have in common!

1 Name the Beatles song performed by Ringo Starr, which inspired a feature-length cartoon film?

2 Which object was seen as a symbol of cowardice and often handed to men who abstained from war?

3 Where does the President of the United States reside?

4 Which Oscar-winning film starred Natalie Portman as a ballerina?

5 The name of Mick Hucknall's band?

6 Name the series of films featuring Inspector Jacques Clouseau?

7 Name the saucy book which has sold more than 5.3 million copies in the UK?

8 What was the name of the first Sherlock Holmes story?

9 Which football ground is owned by Tottenham Hotspur?

10 What were the playing cards doing to the Queen of Heart's roses to avoid trouble?

11 In Californian geography, what does the abbreviation O.C. stand for?

PIC: REX FEATURES

12 What did Dorothy and pals need to follow to find the Wizard of Oz?

13 Which English actress (and former **Yours** cover star) is best known for playing Sandra Pullman in New Tricks?

14 Name the rock band who released iconic album The Dark Side Of The Moon?

15 What – according to superstition – shouldn't be allowed to cross your path?

16 Name the London borough, where the Royal Observatory is based, which marks international time?

17 What's the UK's most common pub name?

18 A five-letter word meaning eco-friendly?

PIC: REX FEATURES

The connection: They are all colours

Answers: 1 Yellow Submarine, 2 A white feather, 3 The White House, 4 Black Swan, 5 Simply Red, 6 The Pink Panther, 7 50 Shades of Grey, 8 A Study in Scarlet, 9 White Hart Lane, 10 Painting them red, 11 Orange County, 12 The yellow-brick road, 13 Amanda Redman, 14 Pink Floyd, 15 Black cat, 16 Greenwich, 17 The Red Lion, 18 Green.

Box of memories... period pieces

Nothing beats a good costume drama, gadzooks!

Period dramas like Upstairs Downstairs continue to enthrall modern-day viewers

PIC REX FEATURES

As Downton Abbey proved, costume dramas are always a sure-fire hit with TV audiences. Long before Michelle Dockery intrigued us as Lady Mary, Susan Hampshire fascinated viewers as headstrong Fleur in The Forsyte Saga. Based on the novels of John Galsworthy, the series also starred New Zealand actress Nyree Dawn Porter as the beautiful but cold wife of Soames Forsyte (Eric Porter). The series was so popular that churches shortened their services to allow people to be home in time to watch at 7.25pm.

Ships and the sea (as well as sex and skulduggery) featured in two swashbuckling dramas of the 1970s: The Onedin Line and Poldark. Although The Onedin Line was ostensibly set in Liverpool, much of the series was filmed in Dartmouth in

Devon with romantic shots of the schooner Charlotte Rhodes riding the waves. Sea sickness was said to be a recurring problem for some members of the cast!

Further west, Cornwall was the location for Poldark, in which Angharad Rees played the scheming minx Demelza, determined to snare dashing Ross Poldark (Robin Ellis) despite his love for the elegant, upper-class Elizabeth (Jill Townsend).

Class differences underpinned the much-loved series, Upstairs, Downstairs which followed storylines on both sides of the green baize door separating servants from their employers. Viewers were as much enthralled by Mrs Bridges, the cook (Angela Baddeley) and Hudson, the butler (Gordon Jackson) as by the Bellamy family who owned the grand

house in Eaton Square. When Rachel Gurney, the actress who played Lady Marjorie, wanted to leave the series, the scriptwriters arranged for the unfortunate woman to meet her end as a passenger on the Titanic.

Upstairs, Downstairs ran for 68 episodes and ended with the marriage of Lord Bellamy's ward, Georgina (Lesley-Ann Down) to the Marquis of Stockbridge, played by Anthony Andrews.

Born to play aristocrats, Anthony Andrews was the doomed Sebastian Flyte in another hugely successful period drama, Brideshead Revisited. Clinging to his teddy bear, Aloysius, Sebastian descended into alcoholism. A star-studded cast included Sir Laurence Olivier and Claire Bloom as his estranged parents and Jeremy Irons as his friend Charles Ryder.

The new arrival

Gwyneth Lowe had waited a long time for a baby sister – but it wasn't quite how she'd imagined it...

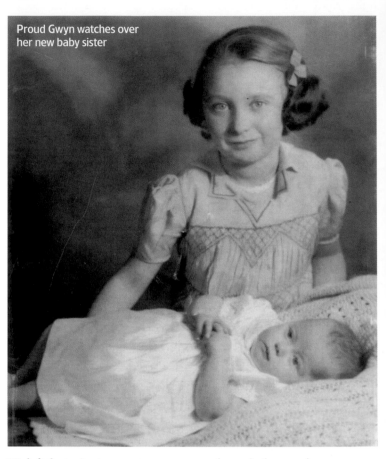

Proud Gwyn watches over her new baby sister

August 1942. Heat, steam and smoke from the trains at the station. Dad and I running along the platform, looking for a space on the already crowded train. "Here mate, hand her up here!" A pair of khaki-clad arms reached down and lifted me up. I was passed hand-to-hand by soldiers packed into the corridor. The train pulled away, leaving the city and passing through the suburbs into the countryside. My father leaned one elbow on the open window, staring at the passing scenery and exchanging the occasional remark with the other soldiers. Settled on a pile of kit bags, my head nearly touching the roof and knees pulled up under my chin, I thought about the events that had led to this journey.

"Where's Mum gone?" I had asked Nan, who was living with us in Dagenham after being bombed out of the East End. "Gone to hospital. She's got a bad leg." I hadn't noticed she had a bad leg, only that she walked very slow and had got very fat! Shortly after this conversation a telegram arrived and Nan told me, "You've got a baby sister!" Expectant mothers were evacuated out of London at that time for the birth of their babies – but it wasn't considered necessary to give a seven year old too much information.

So me and Dad were on our way to see Mum and new sister.

We left the train at a country station, which I now know was Newport Pagnall. The small café next to the station had an abandoned air. The proprietor chatted and conjured up a plate of greasy sausages and chips for dad. I studied the tin plate advertisements for Mazawatee tea, Peak Frean biscuits and Fry's chocolate and wondered when these luxuries would be available once more.

After we had eaten, the proprietor walked us to the door. "Good luck!" she said, pointing out the direction we should take. The heat was bouncing off the pavement and I was pleased when we turned down a country lane

and saw the house where mum was staying. It was impressive, with a flight of shallow steps leading to a huge door, and a high-ceilinged hall beyond.

After a conversation with a nurse, Dad turned and, squatting down in front of me, took my hands. "I'm sorry Gwyn. They don't allow children – I thought they would let you in, but they won't." He looked upset, but the situation was beyond his control. Settling myself on a small couch, I busied myself studying the painting above the enormous fireplace. It was a confusion of plants, animals and flowers. Every time I thought I'd seen it

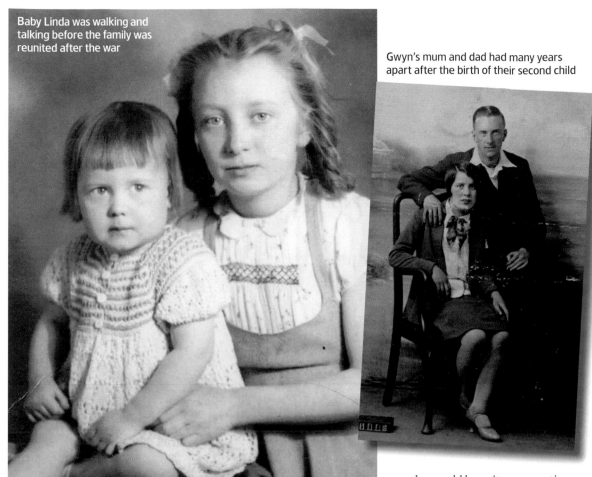

Baby Linda was walking and talking before the family was reunited after the war

Gwyn's mum and dad had many years apart after the birth of their second child

all, another small detail came into view. My mind wandered to whose job it was to light the fire. I was allowed to 'lay the fire' at home. Rake the ashes, crumple the old newspapers, leave a bit of air in them to encourage the flame, then criss-cross the small kindling sticks and space small lumps of coal on top ready for the match. Goodness knows how anyone managed that exercise in that great cavern of a fireplace!

Suddenly, a nurse came running down the stairs with a shawl-wrapped bundle in her arms. "Quick, come and look! This is your sister – I'm not supposed to bring her out but have a quick look."

I peered at 'the baby sister' and touched her hand – I was pleased but really wanted to see

my mother. Dad returned and we made our way out of the house and along the lane. Dad kept stopping and telling me to look back and wave because Mum was waving out of one of the many windows – I couldn't see her but waved anyway. Dad held my hand very tightly on the way back.

A few weeks later we made the journey again to bring Mum and Linda home. Yes, after much discussion, she had a name – Linda Mary. My mother and I had had long discussions on a suitable name for a baby sister, even though I had no idea one was on the way! Mum suggested Stella – "It means little star," she told me. Perhaps, it had some significance. My father was miles away and this was their wartime baby, and my

mother could be quite a romantic at times. But I wanted Sandra – all the best boarding school stories had a heroine called Sandy!

When our train arrived back in London I was allowed to hold the baby while Mum went to the toilet. I gripped her tightly, afraid that she would fall through the bottom of the many shawls and wrappings. I'd waited seven and a half years for this baby sister and wasn't about to bounce her on the floor now!

Before the end of the year Dad was drafted overseas. He didn't return until March 1946 so he only saw his new daughter briefly. By the time he returned the baby sister was walking and talking, and a bit bewildered by this man called Daddy. All I remember is the excitement of having him back safe – and the family being together at last.

A home for Buttercup

BY: JENNIFER JORDAN

The last thing Ted needs is a demanding new neighbour

Ted looked up quickly and cursed as he caught his elbow on the raised bonnet of the tractor. He really was too busy for visitors, but someone was weaving their way along the farm track on an ancient bicycle.

"Good morning!" the stranger skidded to a halt.

Ted grunted. He didn't want to buy anything, give a talk to the WI or attend a charity coffee morning.

"I'm Daisy," the unwelcome visitor said, searching in her bag, "we haven't met but I've just moved into Dove Cottage down the lane and I need to ask a huge favour…"

"Look, I really am very busy…"

"This is from my Aunt Millie," Daisy said, taking a letter from her bag and holding it up with a pleading look.

Ted sighed and, folding his arms, leaned resignedly against the tractor. "Is this going to take long?"

Ignoring the sigh, his new neighbour read: "Dear Daisy, As you know, I am selling Home Farm and moving to a smaller place in Devon. I'm bequeathing Buttercup to you. Like me, she's getting on a bit and can be wilful at times, but she won't cost much to keep. She just needs a nice warm barn to call home. Let me know when you can pick her up. *PS.* If you can't take her, I'm afraid she'll just have to go."

Ted guessed what was coming next.

"Is it possible to keep Buttercup here? Maybe I could rent a cowshed or something?"

Ted already had a herd of cows and certainly didn't need an extra one. He determined to be firm.

"I'll pay the going rate," Daisy said.

"Look, I really don't think…" Ted's patience was wearing thin.

Daisy's voice wobbled. "If poor Buttercup is put down that will be on my conscience forever!"

Ted was in no mood for emotional blackmail.

"I'm giving Buttercup to you… she just needs a nice warm barn to call home"

Running the farm on his own took all his energy so this cheeky neighbour who expected him to accommodate an elderly cow had another think coming.

"I've an empty barn down the field," he heard himself saying. "But it's in a right old state."

"That's fantastic!" Daisy clapped her hands with joy.

The next morning she arrived on his doorstep with buckets and brushes. "Lead the way! I'm going to scrub that barn until it sparkles."

Later, Ted popped his head round the barn door. Daisy was singing loudly as she swept the floor. He asked: "Just wondering when Buttercup is moving in?"

"Aunt Millie wants me to collect her at the weekend."

"How are you going to transport her?"

Ted knew exactly what was coming next.

"Um. I was going to ask you nicely if I could borrow your cattle truck," Daisy confessed.

Ted looked at her slight figure – there was no way she'd manage the cumbersome steering on his ancient truck. He sighed. He really couldn't spare time to drive 50 miles to collect a geriatric cow.

"Shall I pick you up on Saturday morning?" he heard himself saying.

"You are the nicest farmer I know!" beamed Daisy.

Aunt Millie hurried down the path to meet them as Ted expertly reversed the truck through the gate. She produced coffee and flapjacks before leading them over to the rickety old cowshed. As they approached, Daisy felt a sudden rush of affection for Buttercup and couldn't wait to settle her into Ted's spacious barn that she'd lined with fresh straw and (to Ted's amusement) a soft tartan rug.

"Here we are, Buttercup darling!" trilled Aunt Millie. "Meet your new mummy!"

As their eyes adjusted to the gloom, Daisy's heart plummeted. In front of them was a grubby yellow car.

"You will look after her, won't you, dear?" Aunt Millie said as she handed over the keys. Daisy

ILLUSTRATION: KATE DAVIES

He really couldn't spare time to drive 50 miles to collect a geriatric cow

nodded dumbly while Ted went to fetch the truck. The car's tax disc was out of date so it would have to be towed back.

As he drove home, Ted still felt peeved at missing a day's work but the sight of Daisy balancing another of her aunt's offerings, an overweight black cat in a basket, on her lap made him smile.

"Did you want a cat?"

"I couldn't let this big handsome boy go to the rescue centre," Daisy said.

"And the car?"

"Well, a sleek sports model would have been nice," Daisy chuckled ruefully, "Buttercup will cost a fortune to repair, won't she?"

Ted nodded agreement.

A week later, Daisy had a spring in her step as she strolled down the lane to join Ted for supper. He met her with a grin and led her over to the barn. The tartan rug was crumpled up in a corner and Daisy noticed something moving in its folds.

Ted whispered: "Your handsome overweight boy was a pregnant girl – we've got four kittens!"

Later, over coffee, Daisy raised the subject of Buttercup.

"Scrap her," Ted advised without hesitation. The car would need a lot of time and money to make it roadworthy.

"It's stupid to become attached to a car, isn't it?" Daisy smiled wanly.

Ted nodded, knowing what was coming next.

"The thing is, I've become rather fond…"

"Well, I can't promise, but maybe I could scrape Buttercup through the MOT," Ted heard himself saying.

Daisy beamed. "You really are the nicest farmer I know!"

Famous lines

Match these well-known movie quotes to the films they appeared in

1. "Toto, I've got a feeling we're not in Kansas anymore."	A. The Graduate
2. "Frankly, my dear, I don't give a damn."	B. Titanic
3. "All right, Mr DeMille, I'm ready for my close-up."	C. A Few Good Men
4. "I think this is the beginning of a beautiful friendship"	D. Forrest Gump
5. "You can't handle the truth!"	E. The Shining
6. "I'll be back."	F. Sunset Boulevard
7. "Mama always said life was like a box of chocolates. You never know what you're gonna get."	G. Now, Voyager
8. "A boy's best friend is his mother."	H. Apollo 13
9. "Mrs Robinson, you're trying to seduce me. Aren't you?"	I. The Terminator
10. "Here's Johnny!"	J. Dirty Dancing
11. "I have always depended on the kindness of strangers."	K. Casablanca
12. "Nobody puts Baby in a corner."	L. Some Like It Hot
13. "I'm the king of the world!"	M. The Wizard of Oz
14. "Say 'hello' to my little friend!"	N. Jaws
15. "Oh, Jerry, don't let's ask for the moon. We have the stars."	O. Psycho
16. "Well, nobody's perfect."	P. A Streetcar Named Desire
17. "Houston, we have a problem."	Q. Scarface
18. "You're gonna need a bigger boat."	R. Gone With the Wind

Answers: 1=M, 2=R, 3=F, 4=K, 5=C, 6=I, 7=D, 8=O, 9=A, 10=E, 11=P, 12=J, 13=B, 14=Q, 15=G, 16=L, 17=H, 18=N

Box of memories... puppet pals

Puppets had youngsters and grown-ups on a string

PIC REX FEATURES

No one guessed Lady Penelope's role behind the scenes of International Rescue

Ever since 'dear old' Muffin the Mule played the fool, puppets have held a special place in children's hearts. In the early days, there was Sooty with his mischievous sidekick Sweep, and Andy Pandy, waving us goodbye with Looby Loo and Teddy at his side. Also waving young viewers a wobbly goodbye were Bill and Ben the Flowerpot Men.

Later, along came the all-singing, all-dancing piglets Pinky and Perky who, with their sharp adult humour, appealed to mums and dads as well. Indeed, an episode called You Too Can Be Prime Minister was felt to be a bit too satirical and the BBC tried to suppress it.

Many enduringly popular characters were the creations of American puppeteer Jim Henson. He not only invented Bert and Ernie, who still live in the basement of 123 Sesame Street, but also the madcap cast of The Muppet Show. All manner of celebrities, including ballet dancer Rudolf Nureyev, were thrilled to be introduced by Kermit the Frog as 'our very special guest star', despite the risk of being heckled from the balcony by the grumpy old men, Statler and Waldorf.

Stars also queued up to be insulted on The Basil Brush Show. The jovial fox was created by Peter Firmin who based the puppet's posh voice on film star Terry Thomas. Basil was accompanied by a succession of straight men who included 'Mr Rodney' (Rodney Bewes) and 'Mr Roy' (Roy North) who were often the butt of his jokes. Boom boom!

Far from talking posh, Roland Rat dropped his aitches and lived in a sewer under King's Cross station. Despite his humble address, Roland considered himself a superstar and drove round in a bright pink car called the Ratmobile.

A much classier pink car, a Rolls Royce, was owned by Lady Penelope Creighton-Ward, the glamorous aristocrat in the science fiction series Thunderbirds. With her cockney butler, Aloysius 'Nosey' Parker, Lady Penelope was one of the International Rescue team led by ex-astronaut Jeff Tracy. The team's scientist, Brains, invented the Thunderbird machines that were essential in their thrilling efforts to defeat the mysterious villain known only as Hood.

"All I had to do

Jill Maynard remembers how the gorgeous Everly Brothers stole her heart...

The Everly Brothers were so much a part of my early teenage years and, although I 'grew out' of other pop stars of the time, I never abandoned the Everlys. Phil was my favourite – perhaps, not as striking as Don, but because of that I felt I stood more of a chance, especially as he was a bit nearer my age. I realised, of course, that the odds of him turning up at the local hop in our church hall were a bit remote, but nevertheless many a daydream took place during boring school assemblies.

I listened to the Everly Brothers on Radio Luxembourg, when the reception was poor and full of crackles and whistles, but that didn't seem to spoil the enjoyment. In 1959 I saw them on ITV and wrote in my diary, 'They really sent me wild! I cried for about half an hour in bed tonight 'cos I love them so much'. The next day I took down the Tommy Steele posters from my bedroom wall and replaced them with Everly Brothers centrefold pictures from my Boyfriend comic.

My sister, Sheila, and I performed a mean 'Dream' together, along with Phil and Don. I sang the harmonies in rather a wavering manner! Dad would refer to them as 'the Beverleys', after the Beverley Sisters, who were also popular at the time. Sheila and I would respond in expected teenage fashion – deep sighs, eyes raised to heaven and 'Oh Dad'!

Their singles were usually double A-sides, with a fast track coupled with a slow one. The upbeat songs were great to jive to

and the sad ones equally as good to cry along with. 'Let It Be Me' was the ultimate love song, but 'Cathy's Clown' tugged at your heartstrings. I bought and loved all the early Everly Brothers' singles. We never thought of buying LPs in those days – they were well beyond our means. A group of us would meet on a Saturday morning to go to the local record shop and choose a few 45s to listen to. There was a turntable in the main shop but if you were lucky and it was already in use you would sometimes get to play your choices in a back room where you could shut the door and have a jive without being seen. We would select a few singles to play and then dance away in there, before taking it in

turns to buy a record.

I thrived on teenage comics with their love stories, and thought they were so full of true love and broken hearts. The Everly Brothers' songs fitted in so well with the teenage reading matter of the time. I can still picture myself lying on the floor in my best friend Janice's living room, head on a cushion, sobbing to 'Oh, What a Feeling'. Sheila, always more down-to-earth, had pointed out the nonsense in the lyrics: 'Your letters I shall keep, the ones you didn't write...' But that made no difference to me!

I was about 14 when I met David, who lived up the road. He was my first proper boyfriend – that is, one who actually took me out rather than just calling for me to go to youth club. He was two years older than me and working. He was also unexciting, reliable and steady – the type that the girls in my comic strips always went back to and married, after a short fling with 'the wrong sort'.

He lived with his Mum and Dad, and I would be allowed to pop in and see him as long as I was back by 9pm. On one occasion he invited me up to his bedroom! He had his record player up there and played me the Everlys' latest single, 'Temptation', which he

was dream!"

Don and Phil Everly were the pin-ups of many a teenager during the late Fifties

then gave to me. When I told Dad he thought it hilarious, obviously finding it impossible to imagine any steamy goings on between the very sensible David and his young 'temptress' daughter! Needless to say the great romance only lasted a matter of weeks, but I still have the record to remember him by.

I bought and treasured all the Everly Brothers' singles up until 'Ebony Eyes'. I loved the angst and misery in most of their love songs – 'Take a Message to Mary' was one of my favourites – but even I found 'Ebony Eyes' too mawkish. However, I continued to

play their old stuff regularly over the years so that my daughter, born in 1968, grew to know many of the lyrics as well as me.

One Christmas in the Eightes I went to Sheila's house. She had taped the Everly Brothers' reunion for me to watch. At first I was so disappointed. There they were, two middle-aged men with none of the charisma I remembered. But then, as Phil sang a high note, he raised his shoulders and guitar in true Everly Brothers' fashion. The tears started, and I was transported back to 1959, lying on the carpet in Janice's front room.

Jill and sister Sheila could perform a mean 'Dream' harmony

PIC: REX FEATURES

Just inheritance

BY: HEATHER WALTON

Peter hates parting with his treasured lathe

As the two of them surveyed the workshop, Theresa said: "You know you're going to have to get rid of most of this."

Peter sighed. She was right. Moving to a flat on the coast had many advantages, but the downside for him would be parting with the woodworking tools he had acquired over the years, especially the lathe he'd inherited from his father.

Theresa gave him a hug. "I know it's difficult but it will be worth it, darling, when we're sitting in our lounge looking out at the sea. Oh, there's the phone! I'll be back in a minute."

Peter watched his wife dash into the house. She didn't understand that his tools were not just possessions but held memories; memories of working with his father and the excitement of making his first piece of furniture. Although he had never made a living from it as his father had done, Peter had never lost his passion for carpentry.

He had been disappointed that their son, Matthew, had not shared his hobby. Matthew preferred computers, which had given him a successful career in banking, but Peter wished he'd been able to pass his passion (and the lathe) on to the next generation.

Theresa returned, looking flustered. "That was Matthew. There's been a bit of a problem with Josh's GCSE results. He hasn't done well and Matthew is not happy. Tensions are running high so I suggested Josh comes here to stay for a couple of days. Hope that's okay?"

Peter put an arm around her shoulder. "That's typical of you, trying to sort out everyone's problems despite all the work we've got on our hands here. Though how we're going to get on with a sullen teenager around I've no idea."

"Oh, it will be fun," Theresa said. "He was always such a sweet boy and I bet he's not afraid of a bit of hard work. He can give you a hand sorting our your workshop."

"Hmm," Peter looked doubtful. "I'm not convinced that's going to happen."

The next day Matthew arrived with Josh. Although the two of them were on speaking terms the atmosphere was thick with words that had been said and would not be easily forgotten. Matthew brought in the bags while Josh made straight for the back garden to play with Ruby, his grandparents' terrier.

"Thanks for this," Matthew said, glancing out of the window at his son. "I really don't know what we're going to do. He doesn't have good enough grades to do A-Levels and I think he should re-take his exams, but he says he's fed up with school. They say 'like father, like son' but we couldn't be more different. He doesn't have the drive you need to get on in life."

Peter said: "Give him some space. He might change his mind about going back to school. Your mum and I will watch over him until the situation has calmed down a bit."

As Matthew drove away, he said to Theresa: "I hope we haven't bitten off more than we can chew."

"It will be fine. Go out and have a chat with him while I make some tea."

As Peter opened the back door, Josh looked round and smiled ruefully. His grandfather joined him on the garden seat and they took turns throwing the ball for Ruby.

Josh said: "I'm not really a nightmare teenager. I'm just not like Dad. I'm interested in stuff that he thinks is a waste of time and I've never been keen on studying."

He threw the ball with some force across the lawn.

Peter said: "Well, I suppose going to university isn't essential, but we all need qualifications to earn a living."

"I want to do what I'm good at. Dad won't see my point of view no matter how much I argue with him."

Peter asked: "And what is it that you want to do?"

His tools were not just possessions but held memories of working with his father

"How we're going to get on with a sullen teenager around I've no idea"

ILLUSTRATION: KATE DAVIES

"I want to make things in wood, but Dad says that's not real work, it's just for retired people like you pottering in their sheds. But I know I could make a go of it!"

Peter turned to look at Josh and saw genuine enthusiasm in his eyes. The boy went on: "I bet Dad didn't tell you that I got a grade A in DT Resistant Materials."

"An A in what?" Peter asked, bemused.

"That's like Woodwork O-Level, Granddad. Mr Soper, my DT teacher, has put me in touch with a friend of his who has a traditional furniture business. He says he'll take me on as an apprentice and that's what I really want to do."

Peter patted his shoulder. "Well, you put your case very eloquently, young Josh. I'm sure you'll be able to persuade your dad. Now, if I'm not mistaken, tea is being served. Let's go in and discuss all this with your grandma."

Glancing over at his workshop, Peter knew that he had found the perfect new owner for his plane, saw bench and cherished lathe. He mused happily: "They say 'like father, like son', but sometimes these things skip a generation!"

What's the connection?

Answer these general knowledge questions and then work out what all of the answers have in common!

1 What was Paddington Bear's favourite snack?

2 What namr did Walt Disney originally plan to give Mickey Mouse?

3 What is the term for a flock of starlings all flying together?

4 Name the famous painting by Leonardo da Vinci, featuring a half-smiling woman?

5 What is the surname of the infamous family which includes Phil, Peggy and Grant, in Eastenders?

6 Which type of car is celebrated in the film the Italian job?

7 What was the name of Sherrie Hewson's character in Coronation Street?

8 Tove Jansson wrote and illustrated a series of children's books about a family of trolls – what were they called?

9 Which BBC quiz show is hosted by John Humphries?

10 Can you name the creepy crawly whose name stems from the latin words for 'thousand' and 'foot'?

11 Which Hollywood superstar was given a Maltese terrier named Maf by Frank Sinatra to help her recover from the breakdown of her marriage?

12 What was the name of Disney's princess who disguised herself as a man to save China?

13 Name the detective inspector played by John Thaw?

14 Who is the 'mystery cat' and 'master criminal' created by TS Eliot who appeared in Andrew Lloyd Webber's musical?

15 Which metal, named after a planet, is used inside thermometers?

16 Which birds does superstition recommend bowing to?

17 Who wrote Frankenstein?

18 What's the name of the dry, tube-shaped pasta made with durum wheat and often baked with cheese?

PIC: REX FEATURES

PIC: REX FEATURES

Answers: Marmalade, 2 Mortimer, 3 Murmuration, 4 Mona Lisa, 5 Mitchell, 6 Mini Cooper, 7 Maureen Naylor/ Holdsworth, 8 Moomins, 9 Mastermind, 10 Millipede, 11 Marilyn Monroe, 12 Mulan, 13 Morse, 14 Macavity, 15 Mercury, 16 Magpies, 17 Mary Shelley, 18 Macaroni. The connection: They all begin with an 'm'!

Box of memories... comedies

Sitcoms – from East Cheam to Grantleigh Manor

One man's trash is another man's treasure in the classic Steptoe and Son sitcom

PIC REX FEATURES

Just the address – 23 Railway Cuttings, East Cheam – evokes memories of Hancock's Half Hour, one of the first in a long line of TV sitcoms remembered with huge affection. Scriptwriters Galton and Simpson went on to create another perennial favourite, Steptoe and Son.

Like Hancock, Albert Steptoe aspired to better things but was doomed to be a rag-and-bone man plying the streets of Shepherd's Bush with his disreputable dad ('You dirty old man') and their trusty carthorse, Hercules (who was a rag-and-bone man's horse in real life).

Liverpool became a swinging city in the Seventies and was home to Sandra (Nerys Hughes) and Beryl (Polly James), better known as The Liver Birds. The trendily dressed flatmates shared life's ups and downs. The downs included Sandra's bossy, snobbish mum, played by Mollie Sugden who lives on in the sitcom hall of fame as Mrs Slocombe in Are You Being Served? Mrs Slocombe was in charge of ladies' lingerie in Grace Brothers, a department store where no opportunity for a double meaning was ever missed and 'young' Mr Grace was a kindly, but extremely doddery old man.

In 1973, accident-prone Frank Spencer entered our lives, wearing a black beret, an oversized mac and a tank top that was too small for him. Played by Michael Crawford, Frank strained the patience of everyone he met, apart from his long-suffering girlfriend, Betty (Michele Dotrice). In the course of filming Some Mothers Do 'Ave 'Em, Michael did all his own stunts which included driving over a cliff in a car and jumping a 30-foot wall on a motorbike. Phew!

One sitcom can lead to another – as when the Ropers who ran the local pub in Man About the House moved to suburbia and became George (Brian Murphy) and Mildred (Yootha Joyce). Like Hancock and Steptoe, Mildred is a snob who longs to be upwardly mobile. In her dreams, she would be as posh as Audrey Fforbes-Hamilton in To the Manor Born. Played to bossy perfection by Penelope Keith, Audrey eventually succumbs to the charms of self-made millionaire Richard DeVere (Peter Bowles), the tenant of her ancestral home, Grantleigh Manor.

My gran, our house

A touching tribute to Joyce Gale's beloved grandmother...

My grandmother Emily lived with us during the war, at Bicester Road, Richmond, Surrey, in a three-bedroom house. We shared a room so my memories of her are very vivid. But what I remember most of all is her large wardrobe, which completely dominated the room. It had a wonderful light, shiny veneer with a huge mirror on it, and at the bottom was a very deep drawer with glass knobs. I could only assume it held a vast amount of clothes, and my fascination with it knew no bounds.

When I was born in June 1939, Gran was about 71 years old, a very round lady of small stature, probably under five feet. That was tiny to us, as the rest of the family were very tall. Her feet were so small that she once won a pair of glass slippers in a competition as hers were the only feet they fitted! Her soft silvery white hair was always curly, framing her round face beautifully. Even if my belief that she owned many clothes was true you would never have known it, as she always wore floral pinafores over her clothes.

In her younger days, Gran had been in service as cook and housekeeper at 10d an hour for the gentry. She was a very keen needlewoman, able to do tailoring, and she often sat up at night making clothes for the family. Maybe she was making them for herself, too, in order to fill that wardrobe! She taught me how to sew, make buttonholes, embroider and knit. She was a gentle soul, and I never knew her to lose her temper, even though we must have

Joyce's grandmother wearing one of her distinctive pinafores

tried her patience at times!

Gran always liked to keep herself busy. She did some of the cooking for us, and watched over my brother and I while my mother, Gladys, went to work for the Express Dairy in Upper Richmond Road, and my father Jim served in the Metropolitan Police at Barnes. We loved spending time with her.

When the war ended, my Gran moved to Tottenham to live with my aunt Emm, where I believe she had lived before the war. Being on my own now in the bedroom was scary, but the large wardrobe stayed and I would often look at it and think of her.

"It's yours now," she had said, and it remained so until I left home some 15 years later.

The first time we visited Gran after she had left involved a very long bus ride. Unfortunately, I wasn't used to the motion and was sick, which meant we had to get off! From then on we went by tube to Mansion House. It was always Mother and I… Dad would never come. He never liked travelling on public transport. From the Tube it was thankfully a much shorter bus ride to the flat where my Gran and Aunt lived. There were two families living in a large house which had been converted into two flats – my Aunt and Gran lived on the second floor. They shared a bathroom with the lady

and the wardrobe

PIC ALAMY

Joyce shared a bedroom with her gran and the large wardrobe fascinated her

downstairs, and her mother who seemed absolutely ancient to me. Every time we visited Gran I loved going through her button boxes, which kept me quiet most of the time while the grown-ups chatted.

When I was 16 Gran became ill – she and Aunt Emm were now living in Twickenham. Mother went by bus every day to look after her. As time went on, she asked to see my brother and me. When I went, she gave me £5 and a shell jewellery box. "This box is so you won't forget me," she said. It was all she had – she never had a pension, as she was too old to

qualify for one. She passed away aged 90 years old in March 1958, and I couldn't sleep at night for weeks. I would just sit in bed staring at the wardrobe.

The funeral came and went – I didn't go to it as my mother said I shouldn't. A lot of relations I had not met before appeared – I just remember all the hats. Gran was cremated and a rose bush was planted in Mortlake Cemetery in her memory. My brother Don was very upset about Gran's death. We were all very close to her and it took us all a while to adjust to life without her influence.

Joyce and her brother had to adjust to a life without gran's influence

But I wanted to

BY: GWYNETH M LOWE

Jenny remembers Christmas past

Making my way to the local primary school to see my granddaughter in the nativity play, my thoughts return to a Christmas more than 40 years ago when I'd wanted so desperately to be Mary.

I thought if I held my breath while Miss Williams gave out the parts, I'd be chosen. Miss Williams had the unenviable task of trying to find every child in the class a role in the end-of-term production. Somehow I knew I wouldn't be Mary, just as surely as I knew that Sally Harrison would be. Sally had blonde curls and blue eyes while my hair was black and 'straight as a yard of pump water' as my Nan used to say.

When all the parts had been allocated, I realised I wasn't going to get my second choice of being one of the three kings. I'd fancied the gold crown and the beautifully carved gift box. I wasn't even asked to be a sheep!

I looked hopefully at Miss Williams. Had she forgotten me? She smiled in my direction. "I've got something for you to do, Jenny. We'll talk about it tomorrow."

"I wasn't picked," I told Mum and Dad that evening.

"I know the feeling," Dad said as he sat at the table scanning the situations vacant pages of the local paper.

Mum patted him on the shoulder. "Don't worry, love. Things will work out."

I remember thinking how sad Dad had been since he didn't have to go to work every day. In my innocence I'd thought everyone was glad when they announced the pit was going to close because there had been marches and banners and brass bands. People stood on boxes and made speeches and were cheered enthusiastically by the crowd.

But gradually I realised that it wasn't a good

"I'm going to be the Narrator and that's a very important part"

thing. Life was different and our street changed as people moved away. We had to move to a smaller house called a mobile home. Dad's friend Tommy Watkins let us live there; it was in the middle of one of his fields and our nearest neighbours were sheep.

I didn't know what mobile meant so I looked it up. The dictionary said 'to move or to travel'. Well, our house didn't travel, but I liked it. It gave me a feeling of security when I was curled up in bed listening to the rain because I could hear the familiar sounds of the TV and Mum doing the washing up.

be Mary!

and cheering. It was a triumph and Miss Williams said she was very proud of us all. Afterwards, when we went outside, it was snowing.

On Christmas morning, I was already awake and examining the contents of my stocking when Nan came in and sat on my bed. "Where's Mum?" I asked.

"She's had to go to hospital, pet. When you've had your breakfast, we'll go and see her. She's going to be all right, nothing to worry about."

To my amazement I learned that I had a bonny baby brother and he had put in an appearance very early that morning. Later, when Mum and Dad asked me what name I would like for him, I said: "Well, if he'd been a sister I would like Mary, but he can't be Mary so I think Joseph would be good." He was our Joe from then on.

As Joe was the first baby born on Christmas Day that year, our story was in the local paper with a picture. The report commented that 'some things didn't change' and there was 'still no room at the inn'. But, happily, things did change for our family. Dad found a job and we moved to another town and a brand new home where Joe and I grew up.

Sitting in the school hall watching my pretty blonde granddaughter playing Mary, I reflect how very different things are now. The boy playing Joseph changes a wheel on their beat-up old Ford Fiesta and the innkeeper tells him: "Sorry, bruv – no room for you here." The wise men sing a rap version of We Three Kings and baby Jesus is wearing a disposable nappy.

The story may have been updated, but looking round at all the misty-eyed parents taking photos on their mobile phones, I realise that the nativity play still weaves the same old magic as it did so long ago.

The next evening I told Nan excitedly: "I'm going to be the Narrator and that's a very important part. Miss Williams said it was because I'm a good speaker."

"Well, there's a surprise," Nan laughed. She popped in to see us a couple of times a week and always brought a big bag of shopping. When Mum said she really shouldn't, she'd reply: "They were all bogofs so I didn't have to pay." I didn't understand how that worked exactly, but it was nice to have chocolate biscuits for a change.

Mum was very tired and had to rest a lot, but she came with Dad and Nan to see our nativity play. I could see them in the audience, clapping

Quirky quizzes

Who said it?

Match the quotes to the famous folk behind them

PIC: REX FEATURES

1 "Beneath the makeup and behind the smile I am just a girl who wishes for the world."

2 "This power that I'm supposed to have over women was never noticed when I was a stage actor on Broadway. I don't know when I got it. And by God, I can't explain it."

3 "Some cause happiness wherever they go; others whenever they go."

4 "I may be drunk, Miss, but in the morning I will be sober and you will still be ugly."

5 "My goal is simple. It is a complete understanding of the universe, why it is as it is and why it exists at all."

6 "As you grow older, you will discover that you have two hands, one for helping yourself, the other for helping others."

7 "I'm never pleased with anything, I'm a perfectionist, it's part of who I am."

8 "There are three hundred and sixty-four days when you might get un-birthday presents, and only one for birthday presents, you know."

9 "A girl should be two things: classy and fabulous."

10 "Education is the most powerful weapon which you can use to change the world."

11 "They say it is better to be poor and happy than rich and miserable, but how about a compromise like moderately rich and just moody?"

12 "An American monkey, after getting drunk on brandy, would never touch it again, and thus is much wiser than most men."

13 "You can't stay in your corner of the forest waiting for others to come to you. You have to go to them sometimes."

14 "I have a very strict gun control policy: if there's a gun around, I want to be in control of it."

15 "I have frequently gained my first real insight into the character of parents by studying their children."

16 "The hunger for love is much more difficult to remove than the hunger for bread."

17 "The length of a film should be directly related to the endurance of the human bladder."

18 "I was very, very under-developed for my age, I hated what I looked like, so I thought everyone had gone stark raving mad."

19 "You only live once, but if you do it right, once is enough."

20 "Only two things are infinite, the universe and human stupidity, and I'm not sure about the former."

A Princess Diana,
B Professor Stephen Hawkin
C Clint Eastwood
D Lewis Carroll
E Mother Teresa
F Coco Chanel
G Audrey Hepburn
H Alfred Hitchcock
I Mae West
J Marilyn Monroe
K Charles Darwin
L Twiggy
M Clark Gable
N Arthur Conan Doyle
O Michael Jackson
P Oscar Wilde
Q AA Milne
R Nelson Mandela
S Albert Einstein
T Winston Churchill

Answers: 1=J, 2=M, 3=P, 4=T, 5=B, 6=G, 7=O, 8=D, 9=F, 10=R, 11=A, 12=K, 13=Q, 14=C, 15=N, 16=E, 17=H, 18=L, 19=I, 20=S

Box of memories... variety

The great days of music hall lived on in TV variety shows

PIC REX FEATURES

Brothers Mike and Bernie Winters delivered Big Night Out variety

High-kicking chorus girls, a magician, a troupe of acrobats, a comedian, a popular singer – variety shows had something for all ages and tastes. The first Sunday Night at the London Palladium in 1955 was hosted by Tommy Trinder and 'Our Gracie' (Gracie Fields) topped the bill. Over the years a succession of famous hosts included Bob Monkhouse, Norman Vaughan, Jimmy Tarbuck and Bruce 'I'm in charge!' Forsyth.

On Saturday evenings, fans of variety switched on to be hailed with a yell of 'Wakey Wakey!' from chubby band leader Billy Cotton. Billy's resident vocalists were Kathie Kay (always introduced as 'the beautiful Kathie Kay') and Alan Breeze (who sang 'I've Got a Lovely Bunch of Coconuts' with a true Londoner's gusto).

Before political correctness was invented, The Black and White Minstrel Show starred the George Mitchell Singers wearing black make-up on their faces. Despite complaints of racism, the show was a great success and ran for 20 years. Comedy was provided by Stan Stennett and Leslie Crowther (of Crackerjack fame) and glamour by the all-dancing Television Toppers and the Scottish singer Margo Henderson.

In the Seventies, Seaside Special was a variety show broadcast from a big top set up at various seaside resorts around the country. Hosted by radio DJs such as Noel Edmonds and Tony Blackburn, it featured everyone from The New Seekers to Val Doonican and Windsor Davies

and Don Estelle (from It Ain't Half Hot, Mum) singing Whispering Grass. Comedians Mike and Bernie Winters appeared on Seaside Special and also hosted their own variety shows, Big Night Out and Blackpool Night Out. In 1967 they had a series called Mike and Bernie's Music Hall.

Of course, music hall was where it all started and for thirty years TV celebrated variety's theatrical origins in a programme called The Good Old Days. The chairman, Leonard Sachs, specialised in using extraordinarily long words to introduce the acts and the audience (all dressed in suitable period costume) responded with appreciative 'Ooohs' and 'Aaahs'. Every show ended with everyone joyfully singing Down at the Old Bull and Bush.

We're all going on a

For Sheila Mills, school holidays meant heading off to her family's much-loved caravan on the Devon coast...

It may have been basic accommodation but holidays were magical in Sheila's family caravan

I have fond memories of caravan holidays in the Fifties, spent with my parents and our wonderful tabby cat, Prince! Our van was not on a normal caravan site, but in a wooded area in the grounds of a hotel, so it felt very special. Prince enjoyed the freedom of the woods, but never strayed away from us.

My father was a sign artist running his own business, and therefore spent long hours working to support his family. My mother was the instigator of having a caravan as she thought it would provide a bolthole for my father away from his demanding work. Our home was ten miles away in Exeter. Travel to get to our destination was by steam train, arriving at a station in Dawlish Warren, a quaint little seaside place and not at all commercialised in those days. We walked from the station with our bags, with the exception of during the school summer holidays, when we spent three glorious weeks at our caravan, and my father would arrange for a local taxi to pick us up on account of all our extra baggage – cat in basket included, of course!

The caravan itself was basic but magical in my eyes. It was neatly fitted out with lounge seating that miraculously converted into two bunk beds. On the opposite wall there was a double bed which was stored in the wall and came out on a spring system when needed.

There were cupboards for storage that almost touched the ceiling, and a double wardrobe to put our clothes in. There was a kitchen area with a sink and draining board, and a small cooker with a hob and oven fuelled by a propane gas container which lived outside. Lighting throughout was by gas – I remember the little mantels were delicate to touch, covered by glass bowls. We also had a smokeless fuel stove to heat the caravan on the colder days. There was even an indoor toilet – the Elsan type whereby chemicals had to be used to break down the waste products!

Surrounding the caravan was interwoven fencing, which was originally put up because the hotel owner had an adjoining smallholding. A large sow escaped one day from its sty and chose to explore the outside of our caravan – we were all terrified that she would tip it off balance! Hence the fence soon went up!

I used to help the hotel

summer holiday...

A woven fence was erected around the caravan after a close encounter with an escaped sow

manager's brother feed the chickens and pigs at the smallholding. Scraps of food (imagine the waste from a hotel!) would be boiled up in a container to make pigswill that the pigs loved. The chickens would all run towards you when they saw you holding a bucket, too! There was also a gorgeous terrier dog called Topsy which always seemed to be having puppies, but my mother would not let me have one, however much I pleaded with her!

We were also lucky enough to have a beach hut nearby, which my father had made by a carpenter friend. It was lovely to have somewhere to change from clothing into swimming suits, to shelter when the sun was very hot (and from the rain). My mother forever had the kettle boiling and would be making sandwiches containing fish paste filling or corned beef with mashed potato. There was always a homemade cake or sponge – my mother was a good cook. On a dull day we would have a game of cards or a board game like ludo or snakes and ladders. I loved taking long walks across the Warren, and would take a lovely Topsy with me. The owners had a shop to run and were glad for me to exercise her.

I was a strong swimmer, having been taught by a lady who also had a beach hut. She and her husband were childless, and always made a fuss of me. One day she took me out of my depth and then let me go – from that time on I swam like a fish!

To get to the beach, one had to encounter large rocks which were put there as a sea defence – it was great fun climbing on them.

There were also rock pools where one could see small crabs and mussels. The beach huts were a great way to socialise for both children and parents. The men and boys would sometimes play football on the grass area nearby – I always asked to join in and enjoyed it. At the end of the beach hut season, everybody got together and we would have a party at the hotel, followed by a bonfire and firework display. I wonder if anyone else remembers those lovely summers in Dawlish Warren...?

Recipe index

Desserts

Cakes and bakes

Just for fun

Pedigree®

Visit www.pedigreebooks.com

YEARBOOK 2015

A year with
Yours
from your favourite magazine

CLEAR
WEEK-TO-VIEW
DIARY!

Seasonal recipes
Craft projects
All new fiction
Great days out
Tips and quizzes
Your memories

Pedigree®

Visit pedigreebooks.com to discover more on this year's
Yours Yearbook, plus other titles in our range.
Scan with your mobile device to learn more.

Pedigree Books, Beech Hill House, Walnut Gardens, Exeter EX4 4DH